Band Acres

Kit's New Home

CHICKADEE
WORDS

Bandana Acres
Kit's New Home

Kathy J Perry

CHICKADEE
WORDS

To receive updates on future books in the series, visit Chickadeewords.com

Printed in the United States of America
& Distributed Worldwide by Ingram Spark

Library of Congress Control Number 2018900660

Hardback ISBN: 978-0-9998315-3-3
Soft back ISBN: 978-0-9998315-4-0
E-book ISBN: 978-0-9998315-5-7

Lexile® Level: 650L
Word count: 2,480

Edited by Beth Bruno
Character Design by Mark Baral
Cover & Interior Design by Rachel Lawston

This book is dedicated to all children who love animals and are learning to read. **May you always be honest, trustworthy, loyal, and accepting of your friends.**

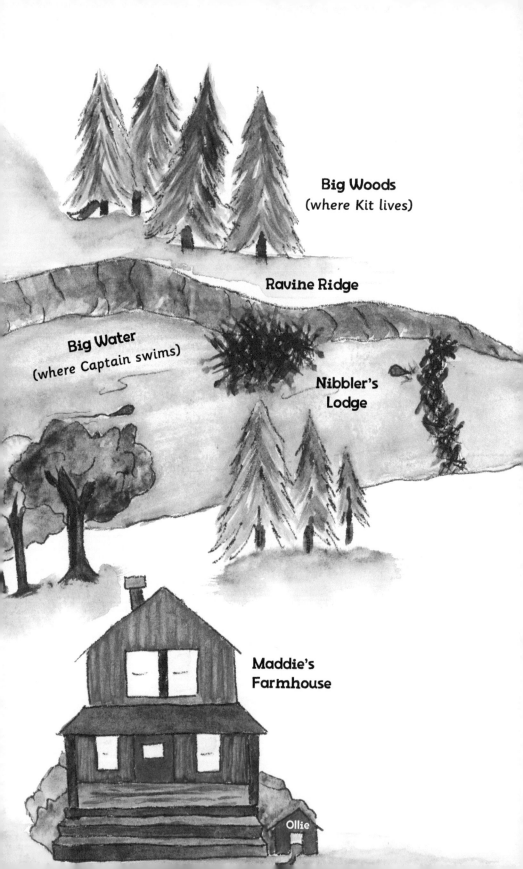

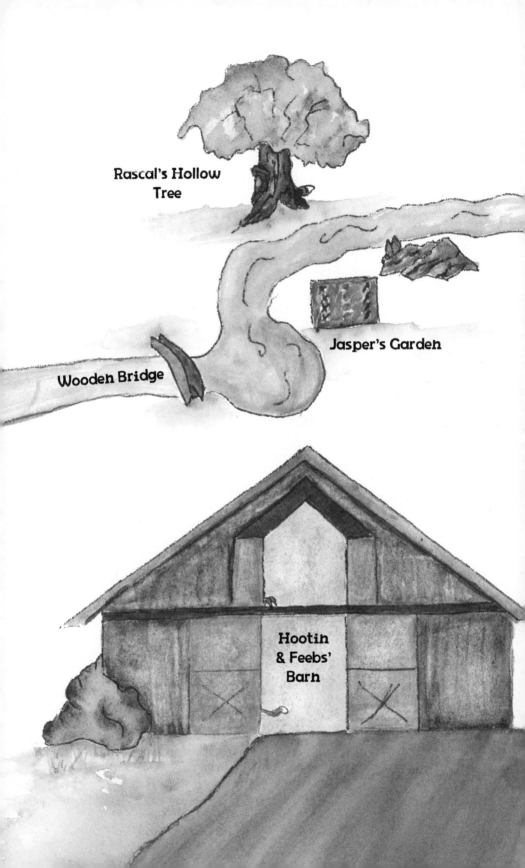

Earning Trust

I wonder where this wooden bridge leads? The red fox scurried across it to explore. She approached a wide open space with a split-rail fence around it. Inside were two mules and a cow munching grass near a big pond. It was hot and the cool water sure looked inviting!

Kit studied the large farm animals. They looked friendly and she was tired of always being alone. **I hope I don't scare them away.** Crouching low, she tiptoed quietly through the grass surrounding the pond and crept in for a drink.

All of a sudden, one of the mules brayed,

reared up on his back legs, and charged in her direction. **Yikes!** Kit jumped back and cowered next to the fence, thankful that the pond stood between them.

"Wait!" Kit said. "I only want a cool drink from your beautiful pond." **Why should this large, bossy animal trust me? I know! I'll show him I'm a friendly fox.** "Hello, my name is Kit. What's yours?"

"They call me Ellis," said the chocolate-colored mule. He lowered his head and pawed the moist ground with his front hoof.

Another mule hurried over to join them. "Who's this, Ellis?"

"Her name's Kit, but watch out, Molly! You nearly stepped on our little pond turtle!" said Ellis.

"Oh! I'm sorry, I didn't see you in the mud, Zartie," Molly said to a small, olive-green oval shell.

Zartie stuck his head out and said, "That's okay, I should have stayed on the rock. I just wanted to soak up some sun in the cool mud this morning." He crawled up onto a large flat rock that stuck out above the water.

"Wow, there sure are a lot of different animals here," Kit said.

"Nellie, the dairy cow, is lying under the shade of that oak tree over there," Ellis said. "And here comes Ollie who guards us from critters like you. Ollie! Come look and see who we've just met."

The golden-colored dog dashed over to them and frowned. "You're a sneaky red fox, aren't you?" Ollie was wary of foxes.

"I've heard that before," Kit said. "But I don't want to hurt anyone. I'm thirsty and I'd like to make friends with you and the other animals. Honest!"

Ollie sat down next to the mules, Ellis and Molly. "Well, we have rules here that you must understand, so listen closely."

Kit sat and listened, giving her full attention to the dog.

"We give everyone a chance," Ollie said. "But

remember this: if you ever lie to us, hurt us, talk badly about us behind our backs, or betray any secrets, you will lose our trust - and our friendship. You'll have to prove you are trustworthy to earn our friendship and loyalty."

"Understood. I promise to be a good friend," Kit said. **Wow! I'll really have to be careful of what I do and say around these animals,** she thought. Kit stepped forward for a long, cool drink from the pond. It was comforting to know exactly what she needed to do to gain their friendship.

For weeks, Kit visited the farm and made friends with all of the animals that lived there. She kept her promise and was a good friend to all, except for one day.

Keeping Promises

Kit watched Mr. Cooper hitch Ellis and Molly to a cart. **There they go again.** Kit wondered why they traveled up the road every few days. She walked up to Nellie and sat in front of her as she chewed on a mouthful of soft, green grass.

"Where are Ellis and Molly going with Mr. Cooper and the cart?" the fox asked.

"The farmer is driving Ellis and Molly to town again to get supplies. I wish I could go on an adventure once in awhile. I just 'moove' from the barn to here. And then later I 'moove' from here to the barn," the Jersey cow said with a sigh.

Doesn't she realize what an easy, good life she has? "But they take such good care of you, Nellie. You don't need to hunt for food, look for water, worry about the weather, or watch out for coyotes. All they ask is that you give them your sweet, creamy milk. And you like doing that!"

"You're right," Nellie said. "Sometimes I forget how easy my life is because it's so boring and regular. The Coopers do give me a good home for which I am very thankful."

"Ellis and Molly will be home later this afternoon. Maybe they will share stories about their trip with you," Kit said.

"Yes, I love to hear their stories. Hey, Kit, would you please check on Zartie in the pond? He was sitting on that big rock he likes, but I haven't seen him for a long time. Please hurry back and tell me if he's safe."

"Okay," Kit said. She trotted over to the edge of the pond and peered down into the murky water. She spotted a few fish and lots of green plants. Some green and brown mossy plants floated on the water's surface on one side. She waded in the shallow parts to let Zartie know she was there.

Soon, Zartie slowly crawled up onto his flat rock. "Hello," he grumbled.

"Nellie wanted me to check on you. How are you, Zartie?" **I wonder why he always sounds so sad?**

"I'm doing as well as can be expected, I guess," the turtle said. "Just hanging out here at the pond. I don't know what else to do."

"It's a big world out there, Zartie. Don't you ever want to explore?"

"Nope."

"Why not? You could visit Nellie and the mules. What about that?"

"No. I don't want to visit them because they don't really like me anyway."

"I don't think that's true, Zartie. You should give them a chance."

"They might not see me, and then they would step on me."

"I'll walk with you. Nellie is close by and would love a visit."

"Okay, I'll try. Stay close beside me!" Zartie crawled off the rock, through the soft mud, and into the grass of the pasture.

They started off together and crept slowly toward Nellie. But Zartie trudged *so* slowly that the fox became distracted. **Oh! There's a mouse by the fence!** She then *abandoned* Zartie in the middle of the pasture of tall grass!

Apologies

Kit caught the mouse and headed back to the turtle. But where was Zartie? She couldn't find his trail or anything. All she could see was tall grass everywhere. **Oh, no!** She sniffed the ground for his swampy, pond scent.

Zig-zag,

Round and round,

Up and down,

Criss-cross

She looked everywhere, but when she reached the dairy cow, Nellie asked, "What are you doing, Kit?"

"I checked on Zartie, like you asked. He was fine, but now I'm not sure."

"Why is that?"

"He doesn't think you or the mules like him. I told him I didn't think that was true and talked him into visiting you." The red fox couldn't look at Nellie's face for the next part. "But he moves so slowly! I saw a mouse over by the fence. I thought I could catch it and come right back, but now he's lost." **I wonder what she must think of me.** Her eyes met Nellie's.

"Oh, dear. That's terrible! We *must* find him. "Moooo, moooo, mooooo." Nellie called for help. Ollie was nearby and raced over.

"What's up, Nellie?" Ollie panted, out of breath from the dash from the farmhouse.

Nellie explained the situation to him. "We should all look for Zartie. But be careful not to step on him," she said.

"Agreed. Spread out," Ollie said. The three of them fanned over the pasture and carefully checked everywhere.

Before too long, Kit found him. "Yip, yip!" she called to the others.

Together, they surrounded the lost turtle. "Are you okay, Zartie?" Ollie asked.

"I'm fine. I was worried I wouldn't find my way home. I kept walking and walking. When I smelled

the pond, I headed that way," he said. He turned his head toward Kit. "You promised you would walk right beside me. What happened?"

"I'm so sorry, Zartie," said the fox. "You walk so slowly…and I thought, well, I thought…" **This was hard.** "I thought I could catch a mouse I saw and be right back. But, then you were gone and I couldn't find you anywhere. I'm sorry I left you,

Zartie. Will you please forgive me? I know I was wrong and I won't do it again."

"I guess so, since you're sorry. Yes, I forgive you," Zartie said.

"That's wonderful," Ollie said to everyone. "All's well that ends well, right?"

"Yes," Nellie agreed. "I'm sure she realizes *now* how important it is to keep your word. Your reputation depends on it, Kit." She looked at the fox for her response.

"Absolutely!" Kit said. "I won't forget. You can count on it." **What a relief to be forgiven and still have these friends.**

Zartie was escorted back to his pond-home. The four of them visited and enjoyed the late afternoon sun. And, yes, Zartie found out that he was wrong too: he did have loyal friends after all.

A light breeze kicked up and filled the trees, blowing their limbs softly. "I think I'd better head home," Kit said. "Looks like we might get some stormy weather tonight."

FIRE!

Nestled in her cozy den, Kit was napping when a stinging, smoky smell curled up into her nose. **What's that smell?** Startled awake, she knew what it was: FIRE! She sprang to her feet and searched for flames. Nothing here, yet, but heat lightning lit up the dark, cloudy sky in the distance.

Right in front of her, a family of brown rabbits and a large deer dashed by. Another deer bolted down the path and shouted to everyone within hearing distance, "RUN! Run as fast as you can and don't look back."

Kit joined the animals fleeing for their lives, but she did look back. She didn't want to leave her hollow, oak tree home. **Oh, no. There it is!** Orange flames licked the tops of the tall pine trees on the west side of the woods. **Maybe, somehow, my home will be saved.**

With her long legs, she sped away. After awhile, she paused to rest as she breathed heavily; her heart pounded. **Sirens!** The fire was spreading, but sirens meant people were there to help smother it. **Where will I go?** There was no time to waste; she bolted east, down the trampled path. Many other kinds of animals fled with her: all sizes of birds, rabbits, squirrels, deer, fat groundhogs, and even tiny mice. **I hope I don't run into any mean coyotes.**

She thought about her solitary, almost isolated life as she ran. **I can always find my way and I've always taken care of myself without any help. Surely, I can survive this.** She passed the familiar wooden bridge and continued east along the banks of the creek. She thought about her farm friends. **I guess the Coopers will take care of them.**

Soon she arrived at an open field. **Uh-oh.** Slowly, she made her way around it. To keep herself hidden, she clung to the tree line. But Kit was unaware of another danger approaching. And it wasn't the fire!

Trusting Friends

Kit paused and then crept over to hide herself in the thick cover offered by a grove of hawthorn trees. The fox's keen sense of smell told her that those dreaded coyotes were near. Slowing her breath, she froze like a statue, but her eyes searched for them. Her ears perked up and caught every sound. The flames roared as the men shouted to one another. Animals made little scrambling noises as they fled through the rambling brush of the forest.

Wasn't she a smart fox? Feeling brave, Kit started to make a move away from the safety of the hawthorns. A coyote howled nearby. Again, she became still as a rock. **Oh, no!** She didn't move a muscle.

It was just one cry, but Kit didn't trust them. Not one bit. Those scoundrels had won their battle last year. She remembered the day she had lost her very best fox-friend to to the coyotes. He had led them away from their den to protect her from their attack. He had fought bravely, but there were too many of them. **I miss him ~ a lot.**

The awful critter howled again. This time it was joined by another. **Aren't they afraid of the fire? Maybe they're answering the sirens.** Kit could smell them. **Can they smell me?** She started to panic.

Soon, she was surrounded by the monsters. As they inched toward her, Kit picked her way through the underbrush in the direction of the creek and wooden bridge. **Maybe I can make it to the safety of the farm. Surely, they won't follow me there.** She felt them pressing nearer and nearer. **They won't get me so easily!**

"Woof, WOOF, WOOF! GRRR."

Wait! That's not a coyote. Kit stopped and peered out into the grassy area. There was Ollie! He was acting ferocious! He frightened the wild things away for a minute or two, but they returned. He continued to growl and bark. If she hadn't known him, she would have been scared to death.

He is trying to help me! Ollie was protecting her and, when she realized that, she ran out to join him in the battle. "BAAARK! BAAARK! YIP, YIP, YAP!"

Together, the large golden dog and the small red fox continued to snarl, growl and chase the

24

wild dogs away. Finally, the coyotes disappeared into the north woods.

Ollie plopped down to rest. "Whew! I'm glad that's over."

Kit looked wistfully back in the direction of her home. "Where will I live now?"

"Well, Kit, I've been watching the people fight the fire," Ollie said. "I think they have it stopped. Some of the forest has been completely burned, but I don't think it will spread anymore."

Her heart filled with hope. "Do you think my hollow oak tree will still be there?"

"When wind clears the smoke away, we'll check. I believe you've earned a purple bandana, Kit. Maddie can tie it on you tomorrow. Congratulations! You're one of the bandana buddies now. You've earned our trust and friendship," Ollie said. "For right now, though, let's get a cool drink at the creek. It's so hot and smoky." He calmly strolled to the water's edge.

Kit stood by the dog's side, looking up at him

every few minutes. She calmed down and began to relax. **I sure like Ollie! Even if my home IS gone, I know he will be around to help me find a new one. After all, we are bandana buddies!**

What If?

Things to Think About

In the story:

1. What if Kit had lied about wanting to make friends?

2. What if Kit had agreed with Zartie about his thinking the mules and the cow didn't like him?

3. What if Kit had not apologized and asked for forgiveness?

4. What if Kit had not made friends with Ollie before the fire?

5. What if Kit had not trusted Ollie when he came to help her?

In your life:

1. What if your friend shares a secret with you? Will you keep it or share it?

2. What if you promise to play with a classmate at recess, but then you have the chance to play a fun game with someone else instead? What will you do?

3. What if you overhear someone telling lies about your friend? What will you do?

4. What if you don't tell your friends what you like, what you don't like, what your fears are, or your favorite color or music? Can they really be good friends?

5. What if your friend loaned you a book to read, but you spilled ketchup on it? Will you:

   A) Tell them you lost the book.
   B) Get your mom to buy a new book to replace it and pretend nothing happened.
   C) Tell your friend what happened, apologize, and offer to replace it.

Glossary

Bray The loud sound a donkey makes

Cowered To keep low because of fear or shame

Coyote A wild animal related to dogs
and wolves

Crept Moved slowly, with the body close to
the ground

Critter A creature or animal

Crouch To lower your body to the ground by
bending your legs

Dairy cow Cow raised for milk ~ Milk also makes ice-cream, cheese, yogurt, and butter

Escort Person or group who goes with someone to give protection or guidance

Ferocious Very fierce or violent

Grumble Complain quietly about something in an unhappy way

Hawthorn A type of bush or small tree with white or pink flowers and small red fruits ~ Missouri state bush

Hollow Having nothing inside ~ not solid

Mossy A type of green plant that has very small leaves, no flowers, and grows on rocks, bark, or wet ground

Mule An animal that has a horse and a donkey for parents

Murky Very dark or foggy

Nestle To lie comfortably close to someone or something

Pasture Large, open, area of land where animals feed on grass

Rambling Growing up and over things in an irregular way

Scoundrel Someone who is cruel or dishonest

Scurry Move quickly with short steps

Siren Equipment that makes a loud, high-pitched warning sound

Smother To cover something in order to keep it from growing or spreading

Solitary Without anyone else; alone

Startle Surprise or frighten suddenly, but not seriously

Swampy Land that is always wet and often partly covered with water

Trudge Walk slowly and heavily because of tiredness or hard work

Wade Walk through shallow water

Wistful Having or showing sad thoughts and feelings about something that you want or have or do ~ especially about something that made you happy in the past

About the Author/Illustrator

Kathy J Perry

BS Elementary Education

A semi-retired elementary school teacher, Kathy now enjoys writing and illustrating early chapter books about animals who learn valuable character qualities. Her goal is to help kids enjoy learning to read as well as apply lessons learned from the animals to their own lives. Her fun, animal adventures will appeal to first and second graders and as read-aloud books to pre-schoolers. Soft, watercolor illustrations have been a source of joy for Kathy to draw and paint. She has a keen interest in art and has designed and created architectural stained glass windows for 35 years for homes and businesses.

About the Character Designer

Mark Baral

Mark Baral, a children's book illustrator and character designer, is currently pursuing his Bachelor's in Studio Art at Pensacola Christian College. Mark has fostered his love for art by consistently drawing and painting, which has enabled him to produce award-winning artwork both at the regional and national level. The process of bringing characters to life through design and illustration has always captured his attention. His love for stories is a great inspiration to him as he strives to create fun and entertaining characters that enhance the storytelling experience. Mark can be contacted at mdbaralkc@gmail.com.

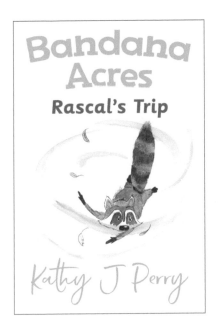

Bandaha Acres
Rascal's Trip

Kathy J Perry

"Oh, no! Why didn't I wait?"

Rascal the raccoon is sorry he ignored the
warning signs. He's surprised by a whirlwind
and he's taken for the ride of his life. Now it's up
to the bandana buddies to help him learn the
importance of thinking ahead. Can he stay out
of trouble long enough to get back home?

**CHICKADEE
WORDS**

Available now!
BandanaAcres.com/book-shop/

"How long will you be gone?"

The barn owlets are hungry! Their mom,
Hootin, must find a way to get more food.
Can she trust her bandana buddies to take
care of her babies during the storm?

Wait, there's more!

Visit BandanaAcres.com/gift/

Be sure to ask your parents before you sign up.

**CHICKADEE
WORDS**

Milton Keynes UK
Ingram Content Group UK Ltd.
UKHW050908230424
441594UK00004B/105

"Writing and art have been my salvation," says Dr. Kendall Johnson, and he took the words right out of my mouth. We look for ways to navigate and live with the complexities and agonies of life without being blind to its mystery and magic. Johnson shows us how to use creative gifts to process, express, connect, survive, and thrive. Blending lived experience of trauma, professional expertise, and a passion for poetry and painting, this unique, beautiful collection will touch countless lives.

—Lorette C. Luzajic, founding editor of *The Ekphrastic Review* and *The Mackinaw*

How grateful I am for Kendall Johnson's "Through a Curatorial Eye: The Apocalypse This Time" [page 58 herein]. What an amazing piece this is—beautifully clear writing throughout and an innovative approach, all in the service of a kind of wisdom sorely needed in the world now. As I read through it I said to myself—this is not just good, it's what greatness is. It's that gift we long for that tears into you and won't let go.

—Daryl Scroggins, writer of fiction, creative nonfiction, prose and lineated poetry, and the author of *This Is Not the Way We Came In* (flash fictions and a flash novel)

This beautifully written and resonant book is a legacy of the heart, from its author to all those who create, be it through the written word, visual arts, movement, or music.... With Johnson's own artworks interwoven through most of these essays, *Writing to Heal* gives us a richly illuminating tapestry of words and images.

—From the publisher's introduction

WRITING TO HEAL

Self-Care for Creators

Broken bowl restored via Kintsugi process by Morty Bachar,
Lakeside Pottery Studio | https://lakesidepottery.com/

Dr. Kendall Johnson

Writing to Heal: Self-Care for Creators

Essays, poems, and visual art by Dr. Kendall Johnson

Copyrighted © 2024

ISBN: 979-8-8692-0312-0

Published by MacQ, Winston-Salem, North Carolina (USA)

This book is gratefully dedicated to my companion, sounding board, wise counsel, patient muse, occasional editor, constant inspiration, and (still, lucky me!) my wife, Susie Ilsley.

Table of Contents

Introduction

by Clare MacQueen

His is an incredibly empathetic heart and calm voice that comes
back from the depths of things not to show his battle scars,
but to show that there is indeed a path out of
the most sorrowful and hopeless of places.

—Dennis Callaci[1]

A confession upfront: I'm an unabashed admirer of Kendall Johnson, the writer, the artist, the exceptional human being. I see him as surprisingly joyful and optimistic, despite the battle scars mentioned in the quotation above, and he's among my heroes and role models. It has been my pleasure and privilege to publish Dr. Johnson's writing and visual art—essays, poems, paintings, and photographs—in *MacQueen's Quinterly* online. And now, I'm deeply honored to present this full-length, printed collection of three dozen of his works, *Writing to Heal: Self-Care for Creators.*

This beautifully written and resonant book is a legacy of the heart, from its author to all those who create, be it through the written word, visual arts, movement, or music.

With insights gleaned from decades of work as a firefighter, trauma therapist, and crisis consultant, Dr. Johnson weaves his own personal experiences into *Writing to Heal* in various forms: creative nonfiction, ekphrasis, epistolary, journal entries, memoir, poems, poetic hybrids, and paintings. To illustrate two of his major projects, *Ground Zero* and *Incendiaries*, he uses specific examples as he lays out his process for creating words and art that "glow," that illuminate the darkness.

His description of strategies that work for him are not pedantic or preachy, but are user-friendly and always accessible. Not to mention fascinating. And he provides practical ways to "help you write your way through difficult material."

Which I believe are especially useful for culture-makers and creators like writers, artists, dancers, and musicians, who want to mine their own personal experiences to enliven their work—yet find themselves stymied, or even blocked, by "unbearable interior fireworks." In his Part II essay, "Diving Deep," Dr. Johnson encapsulates a simplified technical discussion of triggers, including how and why we react to them. And he presents numerous suggestions, along with visual aids, to manage our responses in ways that can help us mitigate further pain or injury, and move forward with our work.

In Part IV, "Through a Curatorial Eye: The Apocalypse This Time," Johnson talks about the dominant myth with which he was raised during the 1950s, as well as modernist aesthetics and paintings by Pollock, Joan Mitchell, and Rothko. This marvelous essay so impressed the writer Daryl Scroggins (also among my favorite folks) that he concluded: "This is not just good, it's what greatness is."[2]

Of course I said, *Amen,* and in November 2023, was delighted to nominate "Through a Curatorial Eye" for the Pushcart Prize.

In the final two essays, Johnson calls for us to use the skills we've learned for important work, as forces for good, and again proffers several specific suggestions, with the goal of creating works in such a way that they "glow in the dark." Yet without causing harm to ourselves and others. We in turn become light-emanating guides, showing others a path out of sorrow and hopelessness, thus encouraging them to nurture their own light as well.

Elsewhere in this book, the author discusses projects and processes by poets John Brantingham, Tony Barnstone, and Joy Ladin, as well as works by artists Matisse, Father Bill Moore, and Van Gogh. With Johnson's own artworks interwoven through most of these essays, *Writing to Heal* gives us a richly illuminating tapestry of words and images.

As Kate Flannery says, "If anyone can find a spark of light in the darkness, it's Kendall Johnson."[3]

With all my heart, I agree. And I offer my profound appreciation: Thank you, Kendall, for sharing your "best light" with the world.

Links were retrieved in February 2024.

1. From an interview by author, songwriter, and musician Dennis Callaci, "Kendall Johnson's *Black Box Poetics* Is Out Today on Bamboo Dart Press," in the Shrimper Records blog (10 June 2021): http://www.shrimperrecords.com/kendall-johnsons-black-box-poetics-is-out-today/

2. From the blurb by Daryl Scroggins inside the front cover of this book. Scroggins is the author of *This Is Not the Way We Came In* (flash fictions and a flash novel), and his fictions, creative nonfictions, prose poems, and line poems have appeared in numerous publications over the years.

3. From "The World Needs More Fireflies" by writer, lawyer, and musician Kate Flannery in *The Journal of Radical Wonder* (5 May 2022): https://medium.com/the-journal-of-radical-wonder/the-world-needs-more-fireflies-3b3dfd9e0e19

Writing to Heal, Part I:

Tapping Hidden Gifts of Experience

Untitled, 2016 (#13 in Fragments series)[1]

I found I'd been left in a field of bones. Many bones
lay about and were dry…. I breathed upon them,
and the breath came into them and they stood.

—Adapted from Ezekiel 37:1-10[2]

Everyone has their own Ground Zero moments—great pain, sudden loss, betrayal, disillusionment, or violence—when it feels like your very neural circuitry was fried. Some memories of these are in flashing neon, while others lay deeply submerged.

As writers and artists, we are unique in our capacity to tap those memories as rich resources, gifts of experience to enliven our work and connect us to our audience. Yet there are risks. This is the first of six conversations about mining this treasure, carefully. I'll start with some of my own extremes.

I've been broken by the world, I'll admit. Stronger now at some of my broken places, yet scarred in many ways. After growing up the child of a war vet who brought the Remagen bridge and the liberation of death camps back home with him in 1946, I followed the toxic dictums of family and culture, the rigid definition of masculine adequacy based upon violence and achievement; first into wildland firefighting, then into Vietnam. Upon return I spent a half-century in search of redemption. As teacher, trauma therapist, and on-scene crisis-management consultant, my icon—my guiding hope—has been this image: a broken ceramic bowl with the parts glued back together, the scars and seams shining with resin and gold.[3] Writing and art have been my salvation.

Writing 9/11: *Triggers*

After 9/11, as the saying goes, everything changed. For me it meant working for several years as trainer, consultant, and therapist for crisis teams in Lower Manhattan, mostly in schools. The crisis teams were my people—school psychologists, counselors, teachers, and support staff I had trained over the previous decade to help schools handle emergencies. I also spent time in FEMA headquarters, firehouses, hospitals, body identification centers, and on the street.

Excerpted from my flash memoir *Black Box Poetics*:

> Phyll had stopped early at the District Office to pick up some reports, when word came down that a passenger plane had flown into the first tower in the World Trade Center. She stopped in to the office of the director of student services, who was the head of the crisis team, and was told to help call the other team members. While all of the team planning had the members working in groups of three to six, only twenty members had made it to their schools before traffic became gridlocked. One, only, could be spared for each of the closest schools.
>
> She relayed instructions from her team leader to the others: stay with your school, work in teams of one, do what you can with whatever situation you find. Her school, a specialty high school in the finance district, stood within a block of the Trade Center. She drove in as close as she could get, then left her car and walked across Wall Street into the smoke and concrete dust.[4]

We hadn't anticipated anything of this size, this personal. Four of my team's schools were evacuated through falling bodies and burning debris. Although trained to work in teams, twenty of our people had to work alone that day. And twenty-one schools were immediately impacted.

My journal entry from October, 2001, Lower Manhattan:

> Ground Zero; the still standing skeletal structure, the bones, the perspective, the mood, the chaos ... the pit at the center of the city. When I look at pictures of it, I get visual and olfactory flashbacks. The subway door opening and the smell of burnt bodies and wiring rolling in, fires still burning, the clamor of sirens and big equipment working, the police and National Guard barriers, the memorials, the vacant stares. Faces of people gone, posted on billboards like so many lost cats. People say, "I don't want to talk about it." Then they start telling me stories. Sooner or later they would get around to "the burning image" that stuck in their minds. After they get through that, they would run up against the "what if it never gets better" question. How do I get out of here? How can I make it quit? They look at me and wait for answers.

Another entry, following a debriefing with my team in October, 2001, in a basement near Ground Zero:

> I asked them: what did you see that morning, on 9/11?

> Their most frequent quotes: "terrible things" "everything surreal" "bodies falling" "children stepping over bodies" "smell was terrible" "couldn't find the students" "smoke and dust everywhere" "couldn't see" "kids crying" "couldn't believe how teachers still functioned" "didn't know what to say or do" "noise was unbelievable."

The long hours and distress of absorbing hundreds of horrific stories went on for several years. You might wonder how I coped with my teaching job and private practice in California, only to jump on a plane to New York and spend days with frantic people in dreadful circumstance. My self-care plan followed all the admonitions I give to my trainees: I saw the shrinks, the priests, and spent time with my closest friends. I exercised, ate reasonably, and didn't drink any more than usual. All of that helped.

Untitled, 2014 (#7 in Fragments series)[5]

What helped the most, though, what allowed me to explore the labyrinthine tangle of amnesic fog banks, red-hot memories, and frozen futures, was my writing and painting. Stolen moments in my studio allowed me to sort things out over an extended period, to lay out tangles of interlocking dimensions of a personal past I hadn't figured out yet, a present which felt like towers of layered jello all a-quiver, and a future obscured by war and terror. I was a mess, but writing it out in poems, stories, plays, and song helped me hold onto the hope that some sort of order was coming.

Rumors of War: *Erasure*

During that period I wrote madly. Some of the expressive writing was eventually publishable, following years of revision; most was not. But it got me through a rough stretch, and some of the writing has taken me the intervening 15 or so years to salvage. Interestingly, only a little was directly about 9/11.

For years I'd also been doing intense abstract painting, not understanding why or of what. Slowly I began to see the painting I'd been doing all along in an entirely different light. I came to see the abstraction as symptomatic of someone who was suffering from amnesia and dissociation. While I couldn't remember many details of Vietnam, I remembered the intensity. And I had been painting the feelings, not the events.

The real question was, how to deal with my own psychological aftermath. 9/11 threw me back into Vietnam, on a gunboat on firing missions above the DMZ. And further back to my wild and dangerous days as a wildland firefighter. I was even propelled back into a myriad of murky family-of-origin issues of abuse and loneliness. I could find my way through the days; it was the long nights that were the hardest. Things I hadn't been able to remember were starting to make themselves known. Lost selves were emerging.

Journal entry from a workshop in Cambria, California, 2005:

> I'm up early to try out an exercise we learned the day before. Mostly therapists who do art, we are learning how to help our clients access memories and perspectives that seem locked up inside. While the others catch a last hour of sleep or early breakfasts by the sea, I take advantage of the workshop leader's offer to use the conference room to practice. The room is cold, fog outside the window. I turn on a CD, go through the ritual of music, stretching, and then drawing. I close my eyes and let my inchoate thoughts wander. As we were taught the day before, I clear my mind, focus on the haunting choral piece, and let my body speak through black charcoal onto the large paper. As the workshop leader had suggested, I use my non-dominant hand. I scarcely notice what is emerging. Fifteen minutes later I break my reverie and stand back. On the white background is a design that takes me back to July, 1967. A round circle floats in white space, lines stretching off, down to the left and diagonally above.
>
> I sit down and study this emergent, abstract shape. After a few minutes it comes to me. A head attached to a shriveled floating body, with jutting lines lifting up. A head, attached to a floating body, with intravenous tubes going in and drain tubes going out. I am transported back to a medical evacuation from Vietnam thirty years prior, where for sixteen hours, through a haze of drugs, I was forced to watch flight nurses struggle to keep twenty marines alive. During those long hours several lost that fight.

The combination of music, movement, and non-dominant hand drawing allowed me access to hidden memories my mind had locked tightly away. For the next six months I reassessed a set of abstract paintings which had been produced over a ten-year period. I came to understand that these abstracts are paintings of the truth, if not the facts, of my combat experiences long ago. The flashbacks triggered by

9/11 were more explicit memories of the earlier times. They served as "flashbulb" snapshots, scenes frozen in time, of moments of panic, rage, or near-hysteria experienced long ago. These memories, because of the different brain chemistry designed to help us cope with emergency, are laid down differently than normal memories. They don't play well with other memories, and can lurk out of sight.

In particular, I worked like a rat terrier, trying to find more in the workshop-produced design of the off-center circle with diagonal lines coming in and out. In the end I produced *Embryonic* (2006), along with a set of other paintings that formed a collection with the rudimentary flash-memoir vignettes. These formed my book *Fragments: An Archeology of Memory* (Inland Empire Museum of Art, 2017).

On Going Deep

Little did I know while I was gathering fragments that I was setting the stage for going deeper in my writing, seeking an overarching narrative to pull those pieces together. Finding that narrative is about, for me, sorting and making sense of the disparate welter of experiences I've accumulated. Michael Loveday, in his craft book on developing the Novella-in-Flash, asks the question: "Are we moments or story?"[6] Do our lives consist of a clear narrative arc, beginning with a complication and ending with resolution? Based upon my personal (perhaps not-too-representative) experience, I would argue that our Ground Zero moments usually lack an overarching arc. That arcing web of meaning, if we are fortunate (despite our attempts to impose one through our arbitrary beliefs and suppositions), only reveals itself toward the end.

As writers and human beings, we spend most of our reflective time attempting to discern that arc of meaning. I've been lucky in that my work has given me flashes of clarity. From the muddle that was New York in 2001, I've been able to pull out some direction.

Embryonic, 2006 (in Fragments series)[7]

Writing can heal. It shares that magic with painting, movement, and music, and it pulls from us layers that we can access, sometimes in no other way. Yet it's a two-way street; just as the creative process can pull from you things that you cannot otherwise put to words, so can it call those memories and feelings and insights that you think you have safely locked away and forgotten, into a form that allows you to share your truth with others. And with yourself.

Write your truth. Write to heal; heal to write. Understand that the path to your personal truth involves surprises that you may not anticipate, and reactions that block your journey. In Part II of this series, I'll share some of the mechanics of triggers, erasures, and overreaction, and ways I've found to manage and even utilize them to support the writing process. I will provide both concepts and exercises for you.

Until then, be safe in there.

Links were retrieved in December 2022, and reconfirmed in February 2024.

1. Untitled, 2016 (#13 in Fragments series) by Kendall Johnson, from his book *Fragments: An Archaeology of Memory* (Inland Empire Museum of Art, 2017), page 18:
    https://view.publitas.com/inland-empire-museum-of-art/fragments-an-archeology-of-memory/page/22-23

2. *The Holy Bible*, New International Version (Zondervan; USA: 2011).

[continued on next page]

3. Kintsugi, aka golden repair, the Japanese art of mending broken pottery with lacquer that's dusted or mixed with powdered gold or silver. Highlighting imperfections and celebrating breakage as part of life's journey, repaired areas may signify synthesis and rebirth. Wikipedia: https://en.wikipedia.org/wiki/Kintsugi

   A lovely example of this art form, a Kintsugi bowl by ceramic artist Morty Bachar, appears on the title page of this book. See also pages 120 and 121 for more details.

4. Kendall Johnson, *Black Box Poetics* (Bamboo Dart Press: 2021).

5. Untitled, 2014 (#7 in Fragments series), from Kendall Johnson's book *Fragments: An Archeology of Memory* (Inland Empire Museum of Art; 2017), page 12:
   https://view.publitas.com/inland-empire-museum-of-art/fragments-an-archeology-of-memory/page/16-17

6. Michael Loveday, *Unlocking the Novella-in-Flash: from blank page to finished manuscript* (Ad Hoc Fiction: 2022).

7. *Embryonic* (2006), aka "Untitled, 2014" (#25 in Fragments series), from Kendall Johnson's book *Fragments: An Archaeology of Memory* (Inland Empire Museum of Art, 2017), page 13:
   https://view.publitas.com/inland-empire-museum-of-art/fragments-an-archeology-of-memory/page/16-17

i.

I see the dark through ten thousand stars. Suns and moons form and disappear. Planets break their orbits and careen about, their gravitational pull drawing their neighbors into chaos. Comets, stellar bursts, whole galaxies recombine. I struggle to take notes.

It matters that artist David Kimball Anderson transforms raw iron into celebrations of our everyday spirit.

ii.

From above earth, the endless depth of space surrounds these tiny blues and greens as I fall closer and move into orbit. Landmass breaks into main pieces floating into constant, rotating shift. How do I share how patterns of disruption form shapes, how snake moves over the land?

It matters that writer and artist Jane Edberg transforms personal life losses into community insight and compassion.

iii.

Continents drift and dance through time. Their edges sideswipe slowly, thrusting mountains upwards toward the sun. I must tell the people about how rivers melt those wrinkles back into sea.

It matters that writer Kate Flannery, lawyer and musician, shares deeper truths of the music she hears, with the rest of us who grew up with less.

Writing to Heal, Part II:
Diving Deep

Whether we write fiction, nonfiction, or poetry, we often draw upon personal experience to inform our writing. Yet some things are hard to write. Not just because they are conceptually challenging or hard to put to words, but because they light off some unbearable interior fireworks. How do you forge ahead and write when the sounds and smells and wild imaginings that your writing has triggered in you prevent you from doing so?

In my own writing about difficult things, I've drawn upon lessons I learned and taught while consulting among emergency crisis teams nationally and internationally, in fire camps, field commands, and disasters from Columbine to Lower Manhattan. I am hopeful that they will help you write your way through your difficult material to uncover gems of experience. By practicing what I preached to others, I manage to find ways to keep functioning—including writing.

This discussion looks at why such reactions occur, and ways to understand them to guide self-care. In part I hope to provide insight into how to avoid further hurt. Equally important, I hope to give suggestions about what I've done to deal with my memories, flashbacks, hauntings, and dreams in order to move ahead. This isn't about therapy, it's about going ahead with the work.

How Memories Haunt

Extreme situations and traumas encode themselves in memory differently than "normal" activities do. Like split-second scenes caught by strobe lights, some memories lay down more vividly and permanently. With those memories are the accompanying survival-focused emotions. Trauma specialists call these "flash-bulb," or "hot" memories. Some are conscious but many lie beneath consciousness, and most are fragmentary. When activated by reminders, they often return unbidden to haunt us, and when they do they tend to elicit the same internal endocrine response they did when initially formed. If you reacted one way in an emergency, then you are likely to react in the same way if you are suddenly reminded of the incident.

A *reminder* of a sudden car accident (seeing or hearing a crash, watching one in a movie, or even reading about a bad smash-up) may trigger a flood of the same internal chemicals that had taken place however long ago. Writing scenes of building intimacy, for example, may suddenly trigger flashes of earlier personal abuse. Result: the brain's upset disrupts writing. The mind interprets the upset as immediate threat.

> While writing a short memoir piece about a burn-over on a big fire (for the story "Flashback" in *Black Box Poetics*[1]), I have trouble catching my breath:
>
> *Suddenly I can't breathe. I am hit by the all-too-familiar panic of oxygen deprivation and I can't breathe deeply enough. The acrid smoke smells of eucalyptus and sage, and the room has turned dark. My skin burns through the army blanket I've wrapped over my face, and small glowing holes begin to appear. People near me are yelling.*
>
> I work at controlling my breath, breathing slowly in for four seconds and then holding it in for another four. Then I breathe out slowly for four seconds and hold it out for four more. Gradually the panic subsides and I can proceed with writing the incident.

Perceived threat can be sensed in the external world (perceptions of real threats themselves, reminders, or similar situations that previously proved dangerous), or can be in reaction to internal cues (memories, flashbacks, nightmares, or unconscious associations). Emergency responses are the mind/body's reaction to threat. Seven basic response types can take place in several degrees of intensity. Further, the response types may result in disengagement, or in engagement with the perceived source of threat. Understanding the underlying physiology of emergency reactions gives clues on how to manage them.

The following discussion may be a bit technical, but bear with me: it is important to understand how this works.

The Biochemistry of Survival

Normal brain function is the result of a balanced interaction of a myriad of natural neurochemicals. When emergency strikes, and direct threat is perceived, normal brain chemistry is altered. This in turn causes changes in brain function, in feeling and mood, and in physical capability. Simplified, three key hormones are released in a balanced cascade: *excitors* (to stimulate reactions), *moderators* (to stay balanced and functional), and *suppressors* (to blunt pain and fear, and increase sense of well-being). This powerful jolt mobilizes the mind and body to survive the threat.

While writing a short memoir piece about the chemistry of emergencies (for the story "Grandma and the Bug" in *Chaos & Ash*[2]), I have trouble with sudden feelings of pain in my hands, and flooding with a dozen visual images of similar stories:

When the jack collapsed the VW on her grandson, eighty-year-old, 113-pound Dorthea grabbed the bumper and lifted the front end off of him. In doing so she ruptured two discs, sprained her right shoulder, and tore several muscles. And saved his life. Later the emergency physician explained that she'd been flooded by catecholamines that had fueled her body and endogenous opioids that had dulled the pain at the time, dissociated her awareness of emotions so she could function, and gave her the sense of being able to manage. She didn't panic, and did what she needed to do. The fear and pain all came later.

I stand up, shake my hands, and go make a cup of coffee. I check email, and then sit back down and proceed with writing the memoir.

Things that go wrong in our responses to threat are generally a result of too much of one, or too little of another of the emergency hormones. Response patterns range from fully functional to marginal to dysfunctional as follows:

Functional responses can range between "Objective," "Fully Present," and "Taking Action," depending upon the situation, the result of a balanced cascade of emergency hormones.

Marginal responses are less than fully functional, and are either "Fading" (with difficulty thinking clearly or making decisions, low emotional involvement, and physical inertia) or "Overreactive" (with racing thoughts and imagination; nervousness; intense feelings of anger, sadness, or fear; and difficulty sitting still or even directing actions effectively).

Dysfunctional responses can take the form of "Shutdown" (sluggishness or paralysis, confusion, unconcern, inability to act, even physical shock symptoms) or "Agitation" (random or ineffective movement, shaking, panic, rage, incapacitating grief, and inability to plan).

What Balance or Imbalance Feels Like

The internal experience of each level of reaction is important for writers to identify, as writers often work in isolation. They don't always have the benefit of someone observing them, and need to be able to identify their reactions in order to manage them. This includes their own observation of what they themselves feel, and what their world looks like to them.

These seven patterns together form a continuum ranging from under-responsive to over-responsive. The middle three reaction patterns (Numbers 3-5) in the table below are the most adaptive:

Level:	Feels Like:	World Looks Like:
1. Shutdown	No feeling	Random, surreal, chaotic
2. Fading	Things don't seem important	Out of control, disconnected
3. Objective	Calm	Consequential, but understandable
4. Fully Present (Aware)	Wide range, moderate feeling	Understandable, possibilities
5. Taking Action (Involved)	Focused: anger, fear, sadness	Compelling
6. Overreactive (Over-Involved)	Overwhelming feeling	Compelling, but out of control
7. Agitation	Unbearable feeling	Unendurable

The diagram[3] below is another way to visualize these patterns:

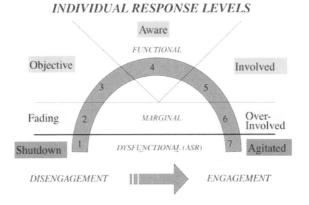

INDIVIDUAL RESPONSE LEVELS

Aware

FUNCTIONAL

Objective   4   Involved

3   5

Fading   2   MARGINAL   6   Over-Involved

Shutdown   1   DYSFUNCTIONAL (ASR)   7   Agitated

DISENGAGEMENT   ➡   ENGAGEMENT

Managing Agitated or Over-Reactions

Revisiting difficult circumstances, whether in the face of reminders, recurrent imagery like dreams or flashes, or as a result of digging deep into memory, can result in marginal or even agitated reactions. Here are signs to look for to identify troubling over-reactions, and steps to take to manage them.

If you are experiencing the following, you are likely becoming over-involved or agitated:

- breathing rapidly

- having feelings you can't explain

- watching others acting in slow motion, or not responding quickly enough

- noticing that time seems to be going too slowly

- hearing others say things that imply you are over-reacting, such as: "Hey, slow down!" or "Get a grip!" or "What's the matter?"

- seeing others as not acting in a way that fits the seriousness of the situation

- seeing the situation as overwhelming

- panicking, raging, or having overwhelming emotion

While writing a short memoir piece about a Vietnam firing mission north of the DMZ (for the story "Home Improvements" in *Chaos & Ash²*), I have trouble with intense feelings of nightmarish claustrophobia:

Cold C-rats for two weeks seasoned lightly with aluminum oxide paint chips from the overhead, loosened by the mind-numbing concussions every night. Beans and motherfuckers and everything looked and tasted the same on the dim red lights, smelling of oil and cordite. Trying not to scream from claustrophobia in the pulsing darkness. We brought evil with us and congealed it there.

Realizing I'm stuck in memories of the pounding concussions and acrid smells, I stand, practice the four-count breathing exercise, and then take a quiet walk around the block. I feel the bite of the cold, and smell the plants. I crush different types of leaves and notice the different scents. An hour later I can go back and start writing the incident.

I have found that in order to slow and balance my own response and moderate my reactions, I try several different steps:

Breath	Slow your breathing: breathe in for a four-count, hold for four, breathe out for a four-count, hold for four. Repeat for a total of four cycles.
Activity	Do some stretching; take a walk or a gentle run, but don't over-do.
Direction	Find a useful task to accomplish; find support and assistance.
Relaxation	Change your setting; sit down, look around you, and notice details.
Focus	Ignore memories and imagination: focus on what is going on around you in the here and now.
Self/other talk	Use soothing and calming self-talk; repeat saying things to yourself that are supportive and calm. Speak with others about what is going on.
Imagery/ expectations	Visualize yourself in a place that you have found safe in the past; write about it. Imagine yourself taking deliberate actions with positive outcomes.

[continued on next page]

Managing Fading or Under-Reactions

Writing projects that, for whatever reason, directly explore personally difficult moments may also trigger marginal fading or even shut-down reactions. Again, here are signs to look for to identify troubling under-responsiveness, and steps to take to manage it.

If you are experiencing the following, you may be fading out or shutting down:

- watching others behaving in ways that seem unnecessary

- feeling little or no emotion

- not noticing your body

- hearing others say things that imply you are under-reacting, such as: "Are you okay?" or "Hey, listen to me!" or "Come on, pay attention!"

- seeing others moving too quickly, or even jerkily

- noticing that time seems to be passing too quickly or in spurts

- not being able to make sense of things

- seeing the situation as unimportant or irrelevant

I have found that in order to energize my own response and moderate my reactions, I try these steps:

Breath	Increase your breathing: take quick, panting breaths for several seconds. Two or three sets of ten panting breaths will oxygenate your system, but don't overdo.
Activity	Get up and move; shake it off.
Direction	Find a useful task to accomplish; find support and assistance.
Engagement	Block memories and imagination: focus on the present. Change your setting to one that requires you to engage with others.
Focus	Pay attention to whatever is going on around you in the here and now.
Self/other talk	Repeat saying things to yourself that are supportive and encouraging. Remind yourself how you have coped with hardship in the past. Speak with others about what is going on.
Imagery/ expectations	Visualize yourself in a place that you have found safe in the past. Imagine yourself taking deliberate actions with positive outcomes.

[continued on next page]

Warning Signs

If you notice either of these sets of reactions (Agitated or Fading) to reminders, thoughts, flashbacks or nightmares, and you are unable to rebalance yourself through the above self-management, your reaction is more than normal. Beyond this point, you should not wander. Specifically, get help from family, friends, professionals, or call 9-1-1 if you:

1. find yourself so disoriented that you don't remember your own name, the date and time, or if you can't recall what's happened over the last day.

2. find yourself preoccupied, perseverating, or ruminating uncontrollably.

3. find that brief flashbacks have become unmanageable hallucinations.

4. can't make yourself stay in the present.

5. are raging, inconsolable, or terrified.

6. find yourself performing rituals repeatedly.

7. are contemplating taking violent action against others or yourself.

It may help to assume that your reactions, however unexplainable, disproportionate, or random they may seem, may point to blocked or hidden memories that are held by your body, if not in your conscious memory. Professionals—particularly those practicing body-based therapies like eye-movement desensitization (EMDR), deep tissue massage, movement therapies, Neurofeedback, and/or art-based therapies—may help with exploring and understanding less-surface layers of experience.

> While writing a short memoir piece involving PTSD nightmares (for the story "Home Improvements" in *Chaos & Ash*[2]), I vividly recall a nightmare from the first year or so of returning home:
>
> *Rolling off the bunk, he would dive for his boots. Can't find them, and he would go down as other sailors dropped from the high bunks onto him. Bodies would tangle and the big guns would fire. Then the screaming. Fighting for his boots, becoming entangled in his wife's clothing pulled down around him as he lay in the closet next to their bed, head ringing from pitching into the back of their closet and from the screams of his terrified wife.*
>
> I find myself ruminating about all of the different ways my PTSD had impacted my first marriage leading to its final dissolution. My wife at the time had suffered at my hands. I find myself sinking into despondency and can't work. I experiment shaking myself out of it, doing the fast-breathing exercise, and listening to some up-beat music. I clear my head, and am able to proceed.

Why Write Difficult Material?

Why go there, you might ask, for what purpose? Why lift and turn over rocks, just to see anew what crawls out? Especially when there's a strong likelihood that more will emerge, new things remembered? Good question, and one not so easily answered. As I wrote my personal, extreme experiences, I used to think I was showing off; dusting off the battle ribbons. Then it felt more like a confessional, a chance to throw light on my personal pitch-dark places. Now, perhaps with age, I am simply trying to make sense of the welter of confusing lived epiphanies—faster than seeing a shrink, better results. Yet I find that even beyond all that, more is involved. I'm beginning to sense that some larger process is afoot.

> While writing a short memoir piece about a difficult encounter with a family (for the story "Revival Sunday" in *Chaos & Ash*[2]), I have trouble with sudden feelings of shame and guilt:
>
> *"What did you do in the war?" asked the young girl. No one in the family said anything and everyone studiously chewed their fried chicken. "Did you kill anyone?" she persisted. "Daddy did." Everyone suddenly wanted the peas passed. Isn't the gravy great? I mumbled something, seeing vaporous souls rising out of the shoreline jungle. No one really knew what to say after that. I could hear the artillery in the distance. The arc light shells flood the midnight shoreline of the jungle with silver light and black shadows. The boat rocks as we drift, waiting.*
>
> Finding myself unable to avoid several similar memories, I get up and take a quick run. During my several circuits of the nearby park, I realize that I need to call Al, my friend from the ship with whom I've stayed in touch. Al always seems to help me sort things out.

I don't write to shock, and am sensitive to the well-being of my readers. If I am going to tell stories that are difficult to write and to read, then there must be a good reason to do so. It is often said that these are times of darkness. Political disquiet in the face of monumental climate collapse, the loss of the familiar, uncertainties of headlong change, all point to a widespread need for reasons to persist.

Many writers these days seem to write to shock, or entertain through extolling violence and pain. I find that totally irresponsible. I hope that I can pull from my own experience in such a way as to touch upon the revelations of human experience amidst the vagaries of the world. I look for the fireflies in the darkness that suggest possibilities of hope.

Going Deeper

We all have lived plot-twists that proved to be epiphanies, or even everyday moments that, when examined, glow from within. Whether we write fiction, nonfiction, or poetry, as writers we pull from our deep wells, and try to put those moments into words that convey significance and meaning. Yet sometimes in the retelling, they pull from us unexpected blow-back: we become blocked or paralyzed, or we find ourselves overwhelmed by memories or wild imaginings. We are tempted to back away from those memories; sometimes we are driven away by fear and revulsion, by what they reveal about our deeper selves. With some focused self-care, we can go even deeper into that which we find difficult.

In Part 3 of this series, I will look at how Form can help us regulate distance while we write personally difficult material.

---

1. Kendall Johnson, *Black Box Poetics* (Bamboo Dart Press: 2021).

2. Kendall Johnson, *Chaos & Ash* (Pelekinesis: 2020).

3. The diagram *Individual Response Levels* was developed and modified by Kendall Johnson during more than 20 years of consulting for emergency service agencies and the military, and has been published previously in books, journals, and training guides.

Writing to Heal, Part III:

Forms for Healing

Plagued at age 61 by paralyzing doldrums, Henri Matisse questioned his direction. Unexpectedly, he received a commission to paint a mural for his friend Dr. Albert Barnes. It was a huge mural—seemingly acres of blank space—over forty feet wide, on a high wall above doors, dominated by three arched windows.[1] All of this complicated his composition. His previous knowledge and strategies, honed by smaller projects—the color theoretics, geometric proportions, techniques of material—failed to work. It was proving to be a fist fight of epic scale between Matisse and his canvas. Finally, he had a breakthrough. In his words:

> Then, at a certain point, there came a flash of inspiration. I took my big charcoal, attached it to the end of a big bamboo, and began drawing the circle of my dancers, from one end to the other of my thirteen-meter surface. I'd got off the mark, taken possession of my surface.... That's how I made my painting: entirely from feeling, without a model.[2]

In order to work with the odd framing, he had to improvise. The successful resolution of the challenge involved turning to his feelings and body, prompting Matisse to grow into what would prove to be a new aesthetic fundamental to the work of his later years. It renewed his spirit and shaped his mastery of form, composition, simple lines, bold color, and movement—foundational to the later work for which he is now best known.

Reframing the Fight

One way we heal is to understand. To frame things—whether paintings, memories, ideas—we place them within a context, which provides a structure of expectations. This aids our understanding. How we frame things shapes how we see them, helps us know what to expect, and determines what we consider their possibilities. When we pull from our past experiences, they come with their own baggage of expectations. When we frame them differently, we can understand them in a new light. Only when Matisse was forced by circumstance to put away his old habits, guiding lights he had followed for decades when composing smaller, less complex fields of aesthetic problem-solving, was he able to deal with the seemingly aircraft carrier deck-sized canvas and its unique setting.

Reframing shifts understanding. A classical painting doesn't work raised out from the gallery wall, nor does a piece of sculpture set behind glass. A story of a child's fright loses poignancy when buried somewhere on page 803. Some songs are better sung with a madrigal choir, some in a gruff chant. Context and presentation are part of the framing and meaning of the piece. Not only is this true in the visual arts, but it's also true in our writing.

Seeing things in old ways, with old expectations, can scare us away from looking more closely. Even the mere association with ideas and meanings associated with painful memories, can bedevil us with stress reactions. (Part II of this series explored ways to manage those stress reactions, should they arise.) In the process of writing, reframing with new forms can enable us to go places we haven't been able to go before, in our recall, perspective, and understanding. Which can open us to fresh inner material. In this way, reframing can work not only to enhance writing, but also to allow us freer access to the self-imposed limits of our own point of view. We can turn emotional distancing into a managed tool to energize our writing.

What Works for Me

As I described in Part I of this series, my work related to 9/11 jarred loose difficult memories of both firefighting in California and combat service on a gunboat in Vietnam. I suddenly could see what my abstract art had been about, and I began to keep an artist's journal regarding the bits and pieces I was reclaiming from the fog of amnesia. Over time my writing came to reflect the greater nuance and discovery. I've found ekphrasis, epistolary, and hybrid poetry to be helpful reframing strategies to open me up to new perspectives. How I see my memories influences how I feel about them, and that in turn lets me dig deeper.

1. Ekphrasis:

Ekphrasis is writing in response to art work. Confronting my own earlier paintings with new experiences gained during 9/11 forced direct encounter with the meaning of the work, and the process became reciprocal: the more I wrote, the more I could accept what I remembered. Eventually, I found the ekphrastic approach helpful in getting greater depth of meaning from the thirty or so paintings I came to realize were really about combat in Vietnam. Once seen in that light, texture, color choice, composition, and implied meaning all came to make more sense. I'd been speaking to myself in a private code, holding memories for when I was ready.

Ekphrastic writing doesn't have to be simply descriptive. Further, it can respond to drama, music, film, dance, and other forms of art. Such writing can use the artwork as an imaginative jumping off point, allowing the work to serve as an opening. A window or a portal within, depending upon where you, the writer, wish to take it. In an introduction to an abstract art exhibit catalog (*Beyond All These Pretty Things*) I'm pulling together for the Sasse Museum of Art, I write:

> Don't forget Hamlet. The great message of tragedy, more than the bad things that happen to us—the losses, mistakes, hurts—is our own complicity. Hamlet, when events careened around him, exacerbated them all through hesitation and overreaction. Most of us need relationship, transcendence, rootedness, identity, and a consistent view of the world. Bad things happening challenge us on those very points of vulnerability. There's a wide discrepancy between our wants and our needs. It's when we confuse them that we sell ourselves short. Our aesthetics require a dash of wild, a bit of unpredictability that tweaks our presumptions and sends us off on journeys into our own deeper interiors. This is one reason we look at, make, and soak in art. One difference between art and simply pretty things is that art sends us deep in there.

During my post 9/11 period, I explored the art of others as well. Vincent van Gogh, long a personal favorite, served to reconnect me with my sense of newfound freedom and joy that I first experienced in the Rijksmuseum in Amsterdam when I was eighteen. The result was a book for the Inland Empire Museum of Art, titled *Dear Vincent: A Psychologist Turned Artist Writes Back to Van Gogh* (Sasse Museum of Art, 2020).

2. Epistolary:

Dear Vincent included more than discursive writing. It was a hybrid project, mixing historical introduction and comment, quotes from Vincent's own writings, and letters that I myself penned to Vincent. Epistolary is writing directly to someone. Writing directly to Van Gogh allowed me a sense of contemporaneity, and also closeness. By addressing letters directly to the artist, whether or not he was still alive, I could deal with social comment, aesthetic critique, and also personal matters, as if he were in the same room. Further, because I could control the distance I could directly address broader issues that at times could be very personal. I could talk about the struggles we shared, our fears of remaining unrecognized, our obsession with trying to articulate something we feel remains just out of reach, our personal vision of the everyday divine.

Dear Vincent,

I'm taking the liberty of writing you directly because I'm troubled about something and don't feel I have the time to wait for answers, if there are any, to find their way to me. The more I learn of your life the more it seems that you might help. Like you, I burn with the need to paint and to write. Yet while you were a meteor, entering the earth's atmosphere suddenly and brightly and disappearing just as quickly, my trajectory seems to have been more gradual. How can I make that jump to where I, too, might someday be?

Soon I'll too be gone.
Maybe we'll some day meet
some timeless moment,
strolling the darkened Rhone's stars
talking of what it all meant.[4]

3. Hybrid Poetry:

Another tactic I find useful in maintaining distance between myself and troubling thoughts, feelings, and past events, is hybrid poetry such as haibun, tanka prose, and cheribun. Because each of these forms employs both prose—a descriptive paragraph (usually a block of print)—and a short, several-line verse, they can be used to explore a subject both didactically (often discursively or descriptively), and at the same time more lyrically and immediately. This combination allowed me to voice my loss of a buddy, Bob. The book chronicles my search for Bob, and how he drifted away through his inability to re-engage with his home after returning from Vietnam. As it did from many others, the war stole an essential part of him.

I thought of friend Bob, how Vietnam had shaped him and all the rest of us. How he was slow to settle down and ended up working carnivals from Sacramento south to Indio, always looking for home. He ran a food booth—hot dogs on a stick. I'd visited him several times. He'd tell me stories of the colorful people he'd met. Then he'd move on again.

transfigurations
particle boogie
dust to mountain to sand

[—From Kendall Johnson's haibun "Moab" in *The Stardust Mirage* (Cholla Needles Press, 2022), with Johnson's photograph of the landscape off I-70 near Moab, Utah.]

These three forms (haibun, tanka prose, and cheribun) have allowed me to approach troubling personal experiences constructively enough to eventually allow me to explore my intense past events such as war, rescue work, and large-scale disaster in my memoir collections *Chaos & Ash* (Pelekinesis, 2020), *Black Box Poetics* (Bamboo Dart Press, 2021), and *The Stardust Mirage: A Desert Poetic* (Cholla Needles Press, 2022). All three approaches allowed me to regulate my emotional distance sufficiently to write more deeply. The point is not to avoid the feeling and truth wrapped up in the memory, but to regulate emotional distance in such a way as to allow broader access to it.

For me, past experiences open up lessons that extend beyond myself, perspectives that I want to share. I believe them to be truths about all of us, and our separate but similar journeys through this world— however beautiful and broken—toward wherever we each are destined to be. To get at those lessons, my way has been to paint and write, no matter the initial discomfort. Regulating the distance between myself and difficult memories through the form in which I write and paint, is simply an extension of my own natural process of dissociation in the face of trauma. Learning to manage that distance has allowed me to get closer to those lessons I'd hidden deeply. Like Matisse breaking loose from his "small painting" rules, my "reframing my writing approaches" shifted my point of view from self-protection to exploration.

Three other writers utilize form effectively to get at the truths they find important: John Brantingham, Tony Barnstone, and Joy Ladin. Each makes similar moves, but in instructively different ways.

John Brantingham and Tony Barnstone: Strategic Uses of Form

In his craft book *The Gift of Form*, John Brantingham tells how he turns to sonnets and other forms to draw out ideas and perspective that are unavailable to him as he works on a difficult subject. In that book he writes:

> When I have an idea about a theme or an idea that I want to express, I generally write it in free verse. When I don't have any idea about what I want to write, I follow a form. ...Formal poetry draws out ideas I never knew that I had.[5]

Beyond his numerous published books, some on many difficult subjects including love, death, illness, and violence, Brantingham served for several years as Poet Laureate of Sequoia Kings Canyon National Park.

Poet Tony Barnstone related to me his own experience of attempting to put into poetic form his intense feelings following an evening encounter with Paul Tibbets, the pilot who dropped the Atomic Bomb on the city of Hiroshima that resulted in the destruction of the entire city, and the deaths of over 100,000 human beings that day and in the days afterward. Tony was dismayed by Tibbets' callous attitude: "They deserved to die." Tony tried to put the meeting into words, finding the free form inadequate to channel his feelings. He recounts finally attempting a structured form, and found that the words ultimately came. By writing from the position of the other person (Tibbets), and using the safety of a familiar form, Tony set the approach and pace that resulted in his book *Tongue of War*, accounts of ground-level participants, both military and civilian, on both sides of the Pacific Theater from Pearl Harbor through to the detonation of the bomb. *Tongue of War* accomplishes what Tony never dreamed possible, both in scope and intensity.[6]

Joy Ladin and Voicing Parts

In her book *The Story of Anna* (winner of the 2022 National Jewish Book Award for Poetry), author Joy Ladin portrays a young woman who had survived the Nazi death camps during her adolescence. The story begins a decade later, as she lives in Prague and works for the secret police. Adolescence is normally a time of identity formation, and trauma during those years interrupts that process. Ladin's character is trying to overcome the effects of such trauma and reclaim her life. How can a character such as Anna be written?

As a trauma therapist I ache for Anna and her daunting struggle. Trauma plays out developmentally, disrupting subsequent stages of growth. We see the lists of trauma symptoms in articles and books, but what does it mean to live those things? To say that the experience of degradation, abuse, and confrontation with death in the camps was traumatizing would be a triumph of understatement. Complex trauma is closer, the loss of a sense of value, self, and the collapse of meaning and will to live. Even more complicating is the fact that Anna was thrust by experience into a pre-mature adulthood. She was too old, too soon. Her identity wasn't shattered, it was malformed.

She was unequipped to deal with the uncertainty of living. Conditioned to expect the worst, the unknown could never be trusted.

Part of the difficulty I wrestled with in attempting a similar process with my—mostly hidden—Vietnam memories was less a matter of recording the intensity of the experience, and more the implications of their meaning. My deep conflicts over my participation in the war, my lingering sense of guilt, my unresolved gender-based issues that blocked my ability to say "No" to going, were churned up each time a specific memory arose. It was as if my accepting even the most innocuous image into consciousness was yet another slide down the slippery slope toward utter complicity and moral self-condemnation.

Ladin's solution to her issue of handling the difficulties of balancing the granularity of Anna's experience with the confounding issues of complicity, survivors guilt, and meaninglessness, found partial solution in form. By containing the most searing parts in verse form, and only later trying to integrate them into narrative arc, Ladin was able to write them truly without having to explain them or work them directly—artificially—into story. Form provided her the necessary emotional insulation and distance to complete this difficult writing.

In a unique, hybrid writing approach, Ladin weaves narrative (diary entries) with sections of verse. The diary sections show Anna's glacial pace in constructing meaning in her life and reason to invest in others around her. The poetic verses in the book serve different functions. Some are flashbacks, some therapy verbatims, and some are incidents related to her existential struggles.

In a diary entry, Anna recounts a confrontation with another survivor who accuses her of now working for the secret police and betraying the memory of her mother and a friend who protected Anna in the camps. Here, Anna shouts back:

Diary Entry, 1 June, 195-

Don't think you know me because you knew her. Don't think you know my Maker, just because you were in the camps. I've never run away from God, old man. If God wants me, He knows where I live.

It's not rheum, it's tears. Hayim is weeping, tarnishing the silver of his beard. Sobs garble his Yiddish. I can make out enough to know it's not a prayer. But not enough to understand what a word that sounds like "mother" occurs again and again.[7]

Verse conveys a timeless sense, related but as counterpoint to the narrative. Through poetic verse Ladin gives voice to the traumatic flashbacks, to memories, and to the staggering implications of the camps that sabotage Anna's attempts to move on. Even contacts with other survivors make hope seem unattainable. In her poem "Song of Songs: Eight Sessions with Dr. Solomon," Anna throws the following memory, recalled during a therapy session, back at the therapist:

From Sixth Session:

i.e. I was liberated
there, in the valley
by American soldiers

when all my Beloveds were dead.[8]

Progressing Through the Belly of the Beast

Poetic expression can be searing. Many of Joy Ladin's lines in Anna are just that, too hot to touch. Beyond that, her story is soul wrenching. Conditioned as we are to expect the fast fix of completion, redemption, and closure by the end of our stories, Anna's suffering seems unending. She sees no reason for having lived, no purpose in going on. Anna survived the camps, but now finds herself alone in the belly of the existential whale. She tries to find sense, seeking it in her childhood and Judaic tradition:

> Diary Entry, 30 May, 195-
>
> My mother used to play this little Chopin piece at the start of every practice—45 seconds of halting dissonance. I asked her why she bothered? She told me that the piece was beauty's opposite, its absolute contradiction. And that nothing she could play, nothing could mean anything, until she made her way through it.[9]

How did Ladin write these lines? During the early stages of writing the book, she looked at the scattered fragments she had written in her early attempts to put voice to Anna, the lyric bits of experience that resisted expansion into coherency. In particular, the fragments stood in rejection of Anna's (and Ladin's) Judaic heritage. They challenged the idea that all was endurable and that the suffering was worth it. How can such thoughts be expressed, and can the way in which they are expressed be less damaging to the writer?

Ladin's turn toward hybrid construction of *The Story of Anna* allowed her both to tell the story and to contain it as well. She could dip into her own experience and extrapolate from her own sense of "otherness" to bridge and inform her characterization of Anna's experience. Literary imagination allowed a leap into history. Ladin's personal history positioned her perfectly for this task. As a transgender writer, Ladin pulled from her own experience of the brutality and erasure by physical abuse and rejection (for inhabiting a wrong body), and transitioning between worlds (her process of redefining gender identity within a traditional family and work culture). By exploring flashbacks Ladin could voice the self-contained worlds of trauma stuck in time, where verisimilitude is reinforced by detail, granularity, and the emotional truth of the moment. Through the distancing allowed her by the juxtaposition of competing forms, Ladin could relate to Anna's experience, voice the complicating pain of memory, and envision her character's process and dilemmas.

The most intense moments of Anna's story, the flashback memories that haunt Anna with their timelessness and feeling of ultimacy, are portrayed in the verse sections where she wrestles with memory images that subvert the promise of sacred text. In "Song of Songs: Eight Sessions with Dr. Solomon," Anna recounts the moment her friend and protector, the Whore, tried to protect Anna from being set upon by dogs. The Whore was shot in the back and fell upon Anna while the dog chewed on Anna:

> From Seventh Session:
>
> belly gleaming like a heap of wheat,
> bullets emerging between her breasts—
> …
>
> The dog's jaws opened.
> I woke up alive again.[10]

Her choice to use verse to voice intensity was wise. Brevity strips away artifice and allows the integrity of the moment without the complications of addressing implications or the larger questions the moments raise. Similarly, speaking from my own experience, healing for writers can be facilitated by getting to the inherent meaning of the event, which is in part articulating its personal and social truth. Writing those sketchy moments can work to pull out further granularity, further truth. It can pull us toward home.

Traumatic experience subverts the answering—and living the answers—of questions such as, "Who am I?" "Am I a good person, or bad?" "Can I trust the world?" and "Do these things even matter?" Whether we are writing incidents, or characters living those incidents, we need to find ways to do so that help our readers, and ourselves, find ways through the questions. Form may channel some of the answers.

Forming Good Writing

To read Brantingham, Barnstone, and Ladin is to be schooled in the constructive, innovative use of form. It is to appreciate the complexity of each human life, the contradictory, layered, and historically informed voices we bring to our unfolding situations. That is what good literature does. You don't write like this to make cheap TV, quick commercials, nor spectacle polemic. Good writing requires hard work and inspired care. Writing like Barnstone's *Tongue of War* and Ladin's *The Story of Anna* delves into the pain and uncertainty of life, requiring the tempering effect of personal distance, not just between author and subject, but also between the convolutions of the subjects themselves. We need, at times, to employ Matisse's trick of standing back, approaching our work differently, and selecting new tools to gain fresh perspective.

Links were retrieved on 31 March 2023, and reconfirmed in February 2024:

1. *The Dance* (oil on canvas, three panels; 1931-33) by Henri Matisse (1869-1954) is on view on the south wall of the main gallery at the Barnes Foundation in Philadelphia, Pennsylvania. See details at: https://collection.barnesfoundation.org/objects/6967/The-Dance/

2. Quotation by Henri Matisse is from "Matisse in the Barnes Foundation" by Yves-Alain Bois in *The Institute Letter* (Spring 2016); Institute for Advanced Study, Princeton, New Jersey:
https://www.ias.edu/ideas/2016/bois-matisse-barnes

3. Photograph, Henri Matisse using a bamboo stick to sketch *The Dance* in his studio in Nice (1931), detail, is by an unidentified photographer and is held in the Photograph Collection at the Barnes Foundation Archives.

   Image above is reproduced from "Matisse in the Barnes Foundation" by Yves-Alain Bois in *The Institute Letter* (Spring 2016); Institute for Advanced Study, Princeton, New Jersey:
https://www.ias.edu/ideas/2016/bois-matisse-barnes

4. Kendall Johnson, *Dear Vincent: A Psychologist Turned Artist Writes Back to Van Gogh* (Sasse Museum of Art, 2020), page 20:
https://view.publitas.com/inland-empire-museum-of-art/dear-vincent/page/22-23

5. John Brantingham, *The Gift of Form: A Pocket Guide to Formal Poetry* (Spout Hill Press, 2015), from the Introduction (page 10).

6. Kendall Johnson, "A Conversation with Tony Barnstone: Writing Difficult Material (Part I)" in *MacQueen's Quinterly* (Issue 17; 29 January 2023):
http://www.macqueensquinterly.com/MacQ17/Johnson-Interview-Barnstone.aspx

   Part II appears in Issue 18 (29 April 2023) of *MacQueen's Quinterly*:
http://www.macqueensquinterly.com/MacQ18/Johnson-Interview-Barnstone-Part-2.aspx

7. Joy Ladin, *The Book of Anna*, revised second edition (EOAGH Books, 2021), page 120.

8. Ladin, *The Book of Anna* (as in Note 7 above), page 78.

9. Ladin, *The Book of Anna* (as in Note 7 above), page 118.

10. Ladin, *The Book of Anna* (as in Note 7 above), page 80.

iv.

Green spreads over earth, algae to plant, micro-organics transforming. Plants then invite animals, and all the higher forms. How can I recount the central part, that all the separate bits of stuff, are destined to return to their home?

It matters that poet John Brantingham transforms moments he finds in the natural world into accessible words that heal.

v.

I wonder about chance, as the wild canyon breath coaxes my senses uncovered. I think about sidereal time, the macro-micro connection, about the larger web in which we find ourselves caught up.

It matters that photographer Susan Ilsley transforms the best intentions of her group of friends into projects for the broader world.

vi.

Dark and light, the canvas invites, waits. My charcoal makes circles and lines first, then shape begins to emerge, defining itself gradually. The studio is cold this morning, the soundtrack fades. Words finally disappear and I become one.

It matters that theologian and writer Henri Nouwen left his bishopric to live in a community shelter with the least able of us.

Father Bill's Studio: Seven Vignettes

i.

Serving as trauma consultant after 9/11 was draining me. My monthly missions to work with crisis teams and leaders in New York —developing new strategies for shifting circumstance, advocating for the fallen, supporting injured teachers and rescuers—pulled on everything I had. Then returning home after the assignment to keep up with my own practice and try to support my family was simply too much. Now it was me falling away, drained physically and emotionally. I carried a dark pit inside me, a void populated by ghosts, a growing knowledge of our failings as a people, a foreboding of challenges to come. It was time to turn back to painting and writing, to rebuild what was collapsing within.

ii.

I journaled religiously and painted when I could. I went to my studio before daylight, working madly until time to get my children up and ready for school. I found myself sketching during school staff meetings and painting in what few hours I could steal. The work was dark, and its direction unclear. I exhibited when I could, caught lectures, visited museums. Something vague and troubling I couldn't see was emerging, even in my paintings. My work was abstract yet something else beyond concrete figures was clearly missing. Itches were going still unscratched, voices unspoken. I sensed a gulf widening between myself and my family. Try as I might I couldn't find the switch to light the void that still lurked inside.

iii.

While having coffee with an artist friend, himself a veteran of many aesthetic battles against darkness, I told him of my struggles. George leaned closer and shared with me a recent incident of his own. Suffering a sudden heart attack while climbing the stairs of his framing store, George had lost consciousness and collapsed. He told me of floating up to a corner, watching from a distance as the EMTs worked on him and loaded him into the ambulance. Doctors later told him he'd been gone for 10 minutes. For a long while he'd been unable to tell his story. "Go see Father Bill, down the street," he said now. "He's a priest, but an artist too. He's the one that helped me see."

iv.

I enter the sanctuary of Fr. Bill Moore's studio.* There, the tools of his ministry are laid out on tables and benches in joyful disorder: pots of acrylic paint, scrapers and trowels, rags and canvas. His massive paintings line the walls. When alone, Fr. Bill creates large, luminous, abstractions that celebrate the sacred within the mundane. When visitors pop in, he generously engages in dialogue, interested less in explaining and preaching, more in intent listening. He encourages his viewers' opinions, focusing on what they have to say about his glowing work. Found bits of industrial detritus—pieces of discarded metal, rusted washers, bent nails—are often found quietly embedded in his work, testaments to a larger redemption.

v.

I kept returning to Fr. Bill's in the ensuing months, when I was in town. I'd stand before his work, watching him talk with visitors. Never did he proffer explanations of how he got glow in his paintings, or what it all meant. He would tell how his father took him over to the desert, how the colors were transcendent, ethereal vast spaces never empty, how wind carried perfume and song, the transcendence, and endless expanse bursting with change. Father Bill would point to a rock or twig he'd brought home, or bits of urban cast-off he had incorporated into the painting. I thought of the devastation of 9/11 two years before, and the treasures he might have discovered there.

vi.

We sat in his studio. Bill told me about his diagnosis. Despite his spartan lifestyle, he'd developed a virulent cancer that had successfully resisted treatment. He chose not to talk about how long he might, or might not, have left. I noticed that he painted with more fervor now, and pushed himself hard. I'd loved his early work: abstract, hopeful, lean and expressive. Now he was in a new, experimental phase—asymmetry and jarring color juxtapositions. Not sure I liked them, I wondered if the departure in style was caused by inspiration or disease. He shrugged. "The early paintings sold so well, and we needed to feed the missions. Now I need to walk this new path while I can."

vii.

The last time I visited, Fr. Bill was in his studio. It seemed bare, missing his clutter and equipment. Some supplies had already been moved to the new non-profit center set up in his name to assist young and emerging artists. Small pieces, 5"x5" and reminiscent of his earlier work, were lined up in process. His hope: one hundred, if time allowed. "A fundraiser for the center," he explained. "The folks in my order were so good at marketing," he smiled, "the prices got way high and most people couldn't touch them. I can make these quickly. I'll sell them to people who need them, or want something to remember me by, but can't afford the expensive ones."

I bought three.

* Father Bill Moore (1949-2020), abstract expressionist painter, in his studio in Pomona, California:
https://frbillmoore.com/STUDIO_IMAGES.html

Link was retrieved on 18 November 2023, and reconfirmed in February 2024.

"Father Bill's Studio: Seven Vignettes" is reprinted here from the online arts and literary journal *MacQueen's Quinterly*, the Gratitude Issue, 20X (21 November 2023).

Writing to Heal, Part IV:
Through a Curatorial Eye: The Apocalypse This Time

These Uncertain Times (2018)[1]

...too much data, too many video images, too many
high-decibel sales pitches and disingenuous political ads...

—Michiko Kakutani, *The New York Times* (09-14-2008),
following David Foster Wallace's death[2]

When I met David Foster Wallace briefly, I wasn't aware of his stature in the world of literature. I knew his wife better, the artist Karen Green, and to some extent shared with her the massive impact of

David's sudden death. But it wasn't until reading Kakutani's commentary that I learned how similar were our views of the world.

Fifteen years later, I'm an artist, a therapist, and an on-scene crisis manager. I listen to my clients' woes as they—and I, and the rest of us —all thrash about in this far worse version of Kakutani's world. In the onrushing Pandemic, Hot War, End-of-the-World now, addicted to a suicidal life style and unable to agree upon what is right, real, or true, hysteria has emerged the order of the day. We don't have to wait for the evening news to watch violence twist public discourse and desperation emerge as basic political capital. Walt Kelly's Pogo proves prescient: we have met the enemy—unsurprisingly, dismally, he is us.

I recall when we thought ourselves great. Our fantasies of historical specialness have long since melted into air. Gone with modern times, for instance, is the nostalgic myth that through our pursuit of personal gain we benefit all of those around us. Adam Smith's "Invisible Hand" appears to be the one slipping our wallet from our pocket, and our resources from the commonwealth, while we have been distracted by the pyrotechnics of political theater, manufactured drama, hypnotic technology, and cleverly conditioned competitive gluttony. Big money has learned it can do what it pleases.

It's growing dark outside and it's getting colder than it was in 2008. Colder than it was when I returned from Vietnam in 1967, to a "home" that was headed for a schizoid breakdown. We need a spark to light our watch-keeper's lamp. In the face of the grinding uncertainty of our epistemic crisis and deteriorating, floating human world, perhaps we could by looking at things differently. As a trauma therapist far too deeply immersed in the cultural present, I can't recognize my clients in the Diagnostic and Statistical bible I was trained to follow. As a part-time artist and writer—perhaps trying to paint myself into redemption—I crawl myself into my studio to seek the alchemy that would save us all.

* * *

I marvel at the myth with which I was raised. The dominant social tale in America had it that the greatest generation overcame the Depression, beat back the Fascists, and then returned to nurture a fair and booming Marketplace. All we needed then, we thought, were John Wayne's fists to set us right. The 1950s, though, were neither simple, fair, nor certain. Post-war abundance was uneven and tenuous, upward mobility—at least for some—was privileged, technology appeared a mixed blessing, and the promise of "a chicken in every pot" had broadened to include unsustainable high-end homes, third cars, boats, and prestige vacations. The house of cards seemed somehow suspect.

We downplayed the downsides. Hate crimes, discrimination, inequity, poverty, unrest, and amoral politics were off set by the distracting marketplace enticements and threats of cold war and warheads. Such was the context of the art of the times, the milieu that gave it birth. Painting, sculpture, music, and theater had much with which to work.

My home town was shaped in part by the art flowing out of its graduate school. Bold experimentation gave voice to the underlying sense of dislocation brought about by the lessons of fascism, world war, thermonuclear threat, and loss of history. While nowhere as spectacle-driven, the 1950s bore disturbing resemblance to where we find ourselves now. Abstraction, developed in Europe by Af Klint, Kandinsky, Malevich, and Klee, hit Manhattan with thermonuclear force. The shock waves even reached my suburban town near LA.

Wandering MoMA one afternoon during my work in New York following 9/11, I ran into Pollock, or at least his *Lavender Mist*. I was seeking more than mute polemic or social critique. Nor did I find him the roaring egotist others saw. When you can't find the words to say what you mean, others may see you as aloof. To me Jackson Pollock seemed on to something bigger than himself.

After Pollock (2018)[3]

[continued on next page]

Dear Mr. Pollock,

I hope you don't mind me writing you directly, however belatedly. Your work leaves me with delicious questions and a few comments. You have said that moving from the easel to the floor was freeing. You can walk around or in it, feel a part of it. Some take that as an expression of pure ego—turning yourself loose from bounds and restraints, letting yourself fly. Yet you spent time studying Native American sand paintings. You loved that they worked flat, and how afterward, they would destroy their careful result. And you knew it wasn't so much the product that mattered. When the sand painter worked, the whole point of it was to participate in something larger than the painter.

Yours,
Kendall

* * *

Once again far from irrelevant, modernist aesthetics provide soulful affirmation to me and voice to my ache in the face of recurrent forces of despair—personal, social, and cultural. The operative word here is soul, our heart and bones, our inner being that goes beyond our transient body, beyond our science, or even religion. Born of individual and collective groan, transcendence and beauty, existentialism thrives. Here in the contemporary confusion that is 2023, we are thrown back on our singular lives, forced by circumstance to fashion our own meaning. We have precious little in common with our neighbors. Our logics are askew; we don't share the same assumptions regarding the meaning of once-precious words like *good, true, evidence* or *proof.* This epistemic disjunct insinuates itself so deeply that the only thing we can agree upon is the meaning of the word *fubar*, though we still argue as to why. The 1950s were a bit like now. After the privations of the '30s and '40s, the outpouring of "buy-me-now" was hypnotic. Important things like justice, equity, and civility got kicked out of the line at the cash register. Letting action precede planning, Jackson Pollock dipped into his body, opened up his soul, and called out to ours.

All was less than transcendent, of course, on the streets and in galleries of mid-century New York. The "Ninth Street Show" in 1951 showed the members of the most prominent post-war artists in New York, The Club. The Old Boys Club. They were all males except one, Joan Mitchell, though there were several hangers-on. What was surprising about that, at the time, was that any women got to show at all. You had to be white and male to get in the club.

Joan Mitchell took Pollock's sharp gesture and released it to speak with broader palette. Her restrained lines channeled explosion into controlled dance; her colors spoke to one another, less discursive, more a spirited conversation. Her compositions weave moments of interplay, progressing past didactic argument, with less shout, and more open conversation. Rather than dramatic cacophony, Mitchell's gestural abstraction became more an invitation to dance, a song of becoming.

My first encounter with Mitchell was in Colorado. I was called to work with the staff of Columbine High School, after the terrible shooting at Littleton. Their despair was palpable, and the effects of the day wore deeply on this trauma therapist, the pain heavy in my heart. Within a few days I had a chance to visit a local art museum and found myself standing before a spacious painting by Joan Mitchell. I discovered I'd been standing for thirty minutes.

[continued on next page]

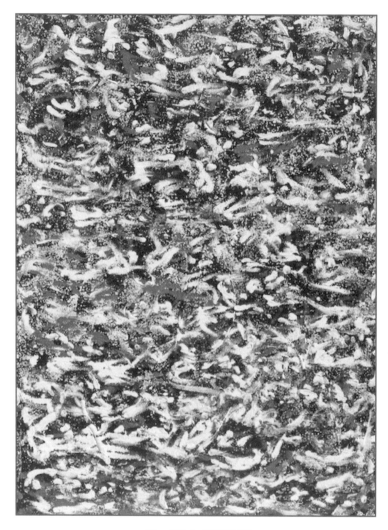

After Mitchell (2018)[4]

Dear Ms. Mitchell,

You do with color what few men were capable of, you dance the margin between forms. You use multiple panels, as independent pieces, that somehow define themselves against each other. You leave my heart, mind, and eye to fill in the logic of transition. And when I stand back in front of your work, I catch my breath. You remind me how I must remind myself, that it is the world around me I must relearn to see.

Yours,
Kendall

I read the news and reviews. Even the notions of freedom, responsibility, and religion feature heavily in the writings of such early precursors of postmodern philosophy as Foucault, Derrida, and Deleuze, and speak more loudly now to a people lost to cyberspace. While out of fashion in some circles, perhaps, such themes persist in contemporary conversation. If you listen, you'll hear they're getting louder. Big questions, like: do we heed evidence of darkness, logics of defeat, and maintain our course blind to light's faint promise?

As therapist and artist I have to consider questions like these:

- Is art-making a worthwhile engagement for those making art? Is "fun to do" or making beautiful, the only reason for having done it?

- Are artworks worthwhile having, either privately or publicly? Can they be worth more than dollar value or prestige?

- Is art a worthwhile community concern in terms of curriculum or investment? Is any purpose served by public art as we ride this errant rock through space?

- Can we seek promise's quiet spark glowing in this gloom? Such small candles in a darkened church, pulling us beyond.

Then there is Rothko. Mark Rothko challenged the sense of dislocation and identity confusion he saw around him as a post-war world struggled to come to grips with revelations of human evil, and to right itself in the face of possible extinction through nuclear holocaust. He experimented with very large format and vast color fields to convey sheer spiritual presence. If color can echo, he speaks to us now, a half-century of rough road later.

His vibrant formless fields of intense color aim at sharing the pure emotional experience. Single-minded in his aesthetic pursuit, he was uncompromising in style and content. When he completed his last set, 16 very large, very dark works for the Rothko Chapel in Houston, many associated them with death. If death is understood as that beyond life, those big dark paintings seem to capitalize The Beyond. Not as a place, but as our context and frame.

On another healing mission to Texas, I looked forward to sitting there in the Chapel, sustained by his work. There were delays and I arrived later than expected.

Dear Mr. Rothko,

In Houston, I stopped to visit your chapel, your last great dark meditations on the coming end. I looked forward to sitting in the quiet octagon, surrounded by your vision. As chance would have it, traffic was backed up a half-hour on the I-10, three lanes merging to avoid an accident on the morning commute into town. Yet it isn't the merge that caused the crawl. We all slowed to surreptitiously glance at the scene, transfixed. Ambulance, blood on the pavement, someone stands weeping in the rain. We want to witness for ourselves, to gaze into the heart of time's ending—the Shiva-dance playing out on the everyday stage. We all peered down into the dark abyss. No one can sit in the presence of your color expanse and still remain unmoved. Tragedy, ecstasy, torment, and exultation all play out in quiet glow.

Yours,
Kendall

After Rothko (2018)[5]

* * *

We know we are bamboozled. So much of the drama and conflicts my friends, family, and I encounter in these liminal days are either displaced energy or outright distraction manufactured to keep us blind to the conditions running our lives. Terror, the use of fear for political ends, is all too often exploited for money, influence, or power by others whose goals are less obvious. Despite the roles we play as cogs in other's machines—my patients, my clients, my family and friends—we are all human. We crave meaning, direction, and purpose, seeking the life-heat of value and integrity.

After my missions into catastrophe, I would retreat to my studio. Painting became my salve, my repair. Yet I—we—need to go further than simply self-care. Looking to art isn't the point. Art as discipline or activity or therapy can no more save us than can science, economics, nor technology. The great take-away is this: If we cannot see the world differently than we do now, we are looking in the wrong direction. We are clearly doomed. We must learn to curate, not exploit, our world.

* * *

Several years ago my friend Yadira Dockstadter curated an exhibit of my paintings. She came to my studio and we pulled out everything I had in store, paintings of various types that I would not recognize as fitting together. From the paintings we'd laid out, she began moving them around into groups that made sense. Much later, the desert paintings graced the quiet walls of a university gallery that opened through floor-to-ceiling windows onto a brush-covered hillside with mountains beyond. Yadira had a curator's eye.

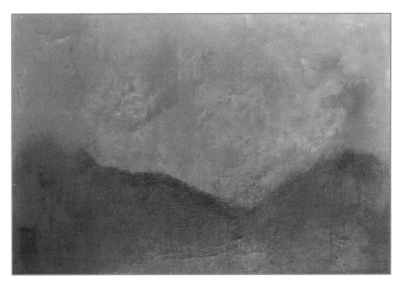

Red Moon Rising (2018)[6]

Leaving the too muchness and spectacle of LA approaching midnight, we drove east over the lonely Mojave, headlights burning pale tunnels into emptiness. This was the old new world, the land of 20 Mule Teams, hidden treasure, and unlimited space. Remembering a voice yesterday declaring, "There's nothing out there from here to Flagstaff," we pulled over somewhere past Barstow on I-40 to change drivers. Stepped out of the car into indigo presence.

> Red moon rising, desert night heat close,
> coyote aria in silver lost light.

These days we do not need the narrow eyes of the true believer, nor those of the cynics who lie for power and profit. We need to see the world through broader vision. Our very lives, and the lives of those around us, are at stake. Instead, we need to be able to see through the eyes of the curator, to apprehend the world's balance, harmony, and spirit. We need to see the whole, not just the parts and targets of our narrow appetites.

We are as much curators as artists, when it comes to organizing experience. A composer like Debussy, for instance, sits at a piano and works out a sequence of notes, including tonal progression, timing, and emphasis. Those notes are encoded on a written page, as accurately as possible. A pianist then, much later, follows the directions encoded on the page.

This is not a purely mechanical process, however. The pianist must seek out the composer's intention within the code, the nuances of timing and emphasis that make each performance of the piece unique, taking into account other pianists' treatment. The pianist, thus, interprets the piece. The composer creates the idea, and the pianist curates the score for the audience, creating the performance.

Based upon our intention and choices, we each progress through the world of experience curating as we go. Informed by the visual, sonic, and tactile sensations we discern, as well as our personal and cultural histories, our fears, obligations, and desires, we make sense of the world and in turn mix, organize, and act upon it. Some of our choices preclude some further experiences, while other choices open up new possibilities to us. We are both acted upon by the world and we create it as we go. We are both artists and curators of our own worlds.

* * *

In the midst of my work on a book about Vincent van Gogh, my wife and I traveled to walk his footsteps in the Netherlands, England, and France. We were privileged to sit with the main curator of the Van Gogh Museum in Amsterdam, who was exhibiting contemporary British artist David Hockney's Woldgate series he had painted of spring coming to the countryside where he had been raised. Dazzled by how the curator had placed Hockney's massive, bright landscapes near to Van Gogh's rather small paintings in a way that somehow showed both to best advantage, I asked him how he managed it. What was his secret, his guiding light?

"You have to focus," he said, smiling, "on the space in between." Eye-opening words, his. A sensibility especially suited for these times. We've been down considerable rough road since Kakutani's memorial to David Foster Wallace, especially lately. It is especially important now to look closely, and to attend to spaces in between.

* * *

Folding back the linen, taking a deep breath
I begin to mix my paint.

Links were retrieved on 8 August 2023, and reconfirmed in February 2024.

1. *These Uncertain Times* (2018), an acrylic painting by Kendall Johnson, appears on the cover of his book *A Whole Lot'a Shakin': Reconsidering Midcentury* (Cholla Needles Arts & Literary Library, 2018).

2. Epigraph by Michiko Kakutani is from "Exuberant Riffs on a Land Run Amok" in *The New York Times* (14 September 2008): https://www.nytimes.com/2008/09/15/books/15kaku.html

    The text of Kakutani's memorial essay also appears as "Literary Loss: David Foster Wallace" in the blog *Slow Painting* (16 September 2008): https://slowpainting.wordpress.com/2008/09/16/literary-loss-david-foster-wallace/

3. *After Pollock* (2018), an acrylic painting by Kendall Johnson which appears in his book *A Whole Lot'a Shakin': Reconsidering Midcentury* (Cholla Needles Arts & Literary Library, 2018).

4. *After Mitchell* (2018), a painting by Kendall Johnson in his book *A Whole Lot'a Shakin'* referenced in Note 3 above.

5. *After Rothko* (2018), a painting by Kendall Johnson in his book *A Whole Lot'a Shakin'* referenced in Note 3 above.

6. *Red Moon Rising* (2018), a painting in Kendall Johnson's Melting Into Air series.

vii.

We are billions, each profoundly unique. History fast becomes reductive to supposed main underlying currents, not the lifetimes of particular waves. Yet who we are is of great significance, to those who love us, and to ourselves.

It matters that poet Tony Barnstone stretches form to convey our complexity.

viii.

Our trail leads through fern-strewn valley, past glacial erratics left long ago. We cross streams and climb past meadows and steep granite slopes. We traverse cold wind-swept ridges. If we persist, we may come at last to the headwaters, the source.

It matters that my son Trevor Losh-Johnson, theologian and teacher, raises his girls well, while he writes.

ix.

I know when a piece is practically done, when I can't imagine adding any more without losing its heart, when its story is something I can feel and can hear. And I know that it is finished when I'm frightened to share, when I've left myself way too far open.

It matters that writer and professor Joy Ladin reveals her realities so as to teach us.

Writing to Heal, Part V:

Writing Hope

Seeking Hope (2023)[1]

Growing up in the Fifties in small-town Claremont, California, several friends and I took refuge from the summer heat in the air-conditioned Village Theater downtown. Popcorn was buttered and often fresh, cokes were cheap, and the Abba-Zaba taffy and peanut butter bars could pull out fillings at ten paces. Ushers smiled, and picked up trash. There were double features, news reels, cartoons. Script writers churned out stories, mostly simple, but entertaining in a mindless sort of way. We ate it up.

Good guys wore the white hats, bad guys the black, and the issues were never complex. The virtuous stood up against evil, and women were victims to be saved. Robert Mitchum, Burt Lancaster, William Holden, and John Wayne all taught us to be ready to fight the Nazis, Communists, and Indians. Kirk Douglas played it all, starring in *The Vikings, Spartacus,* and *Paths of Glory*.

Back then, the Second World War had been won, Korea forgotten, and Vietnam was still in pre-production phase. If we were boys (and then it was less self-construction, more an unquestioned assignment based upon plumbing), we were taught to put down our cap pistols and chaps, trade in our cowboy hats for battle helmets, and sign up for Khe Sanh, Vinh Moc, and the Ia Drang Valley. Later, when we returned confused and broken, when Camelot crashed and it became less clear just who were the good or bad, and who was or wasn't brave, Hollywood's black and white turned inside out and into muddled shades of gray.

Flash forward a half-century or so, and we are again looking for direction and comfort, but are finding less and less. Movie theaters and video streams still pull in numbers of us who are seeking refrigeration, popcorn and candy, and stories that—however fanciful, spectacular, or even apocalyptic—still reassure us that all will work out in the end.

Losing "Normal"

Yet in the back of our minds we know better. Newscasters trade stories of ever more devastating disasters, worse wars loom, the economy will likely crash, plagues are rolling through in rapid succession, deep cultural divisions paralyze our ability to take effective action, fresh water is seriously limited, sea water is rising fast, and the earth and air are rapidly breaking down. While these all may be true, they become background to a deeper foreboding. Words no longer even mean the same to different people. We are becoming a Babylon, each unable to be heard, or capable of working together.

Much to our dismay, the culture wars have weaponized discourse. Facts have become positions, values have transformed into slogans, and conversation mere stand-off between picket lines. We stand on the verge of dissembling of social order, arguing over what our constitutional fabric intended. Deep in our hearts we look for simple reassurance; we still hunger for sitting in the dark together, eating popcorn, all looking in one direction.

What Now Must We Do?

Watching reality play out today, as if it were some inconsequential bizarre video game in meltdown, we as writers and artists wonder if our words and images can play any substantive role in the outcome.

For years I have tried to access memories of my time in Vietnam, on a gunboat with frequent firing missions above the DMZ, serving shadow forces against a misunderstood enemy. Art, both painting and writing, has been more successful than psychotherapy in getting to the elusive truths of my own experience. I am learning to use language—spoken and visual—to find my way. In a combined word/image account of my ongoing memory retrieval process, I wrote:

Abstraction & Evidence

Abstraction serves my art, cutting through distractions of detail and convention and going directly after the truth—subjective, personal truth. Gunfire, for instance. What's relevant for me and my memories is simply what it meant to me. What someone next to me experienced is not germane to my making sense of it. I can try to empathize and understand, but I can't experience it through another's history, values, eyes, heart. The hole in the front end of a .45 pistol varies in size according to where you stand. It can be huge, thunderous. It can stop the world.[2]

Untitled, 2016 (#2 in Fragments series)[2]

How do we respond to our current situation, faced with threats from all sides, possibly including our neighbor next door? What can we do to constructively address a world coming undone?

I spent my clinical life as a trauma consultant trodding news-headline-worthy scenes of mass shootings, natural disasters, and the many ways we humans run amok. My job: advise commanders, treat injured, restore team function. In helping the best of us to deal with the worst of situations, I've been privileged to observe how key people have far more profound effects—for better or for worse—than even they realize or intend: through their words, attitude, and the affirmation and support they bring to those around them.

An artist and writer now, I try to apply that to my new practice. As creatives and creators, we are also leaders, more than we realize. More so, we are uniquely positioned to infuse positivity—beauty, wisdom, reassurance—into the world through our work. Like leaders in crisis, what we do and say can be a force for good. The words and images we produce can help the world. And as co-voyagers on troubled waters, now is the time.

Revisiting Ground Zero

Working after 9/11 was emotionally challenging. I had to stand close to the pain to be effective at helping those who desperately needed to focus on their work. As in prior devastating incidents, as in Vietnam, as in moments of abuse in my own childhood, I used dissociation to get by. That is why it took 22 years to get back in touch with the moment and unlock many of its hard lessons. In the process, I've learned that you can write, photograph, paint about disaster without adding to the narrative of despair. Furthermore, you can discover crucial lessons from the past to bring back to the present.

My past year of 9/11 remembrance and expression culminated this autumn [2023] in an exhibit of paintings and writing held in the Sasse Museum of Art gallery in Pomona, California. My primary goal in the work was to revisit the moment and bring the things we learned (or, more accurately, could have, should have learned at the time) to bear on our present dark moment. My secondary goal was to do it in a way that captured that past without bringing its pain into the present. The artwork and associated writing have been graciously made freely available by founder Gene Sasse in the form of a virtual exhibit, *Ground Zero*, on the museum website: https://view.publitas.com/inland-empire-museum-of-art/ ground_zero/page/1

But how can we write or paint the world's hurt without in turn spreading it, without compounding the damage already done? Regarding our current state of affairs, I'm coming to realize that far too much is being said about far too little. And this compounds our problem. Video images, selective and sensationalized, pass as truth. Commentary and images are tailored to fit polemic and presented as fact. No wonder the media is distrusted, despite how mindlessly it is consumed. If nothing else, our work during this time should bring oxygen to those inundated by media.

We know the "how." In our training and practice as artists, of word or of image, we have learned the skills necessary for important work. Here are some suggestions on how to use them as forces for good:

1. Capture the scene's truth, not just its drama.

At the very least, we can describe things well. Use your powers of prose and poetic device to go to the reality of the situation, without retreating to stock memes and outworn clichés, however acceptable and trendy they seem. The job is to help the reader to see the scene with fresh, newly informed and opened eyes, to pave the way to deeper understanding.

In writing and painting 9/11, I had much to say, some of which had to put into perspective what was already run in newspapers, television, and in movies ad infinitum. What I could show was my personal response to being there, to let my audience in through my boots-on-the-ground eyes. New ways of seeing. My experience of 9/11 was not a God's-eye-view, and I am still learning what to think of it. But whatever the limitations of my perspective, it was fresh, my own.

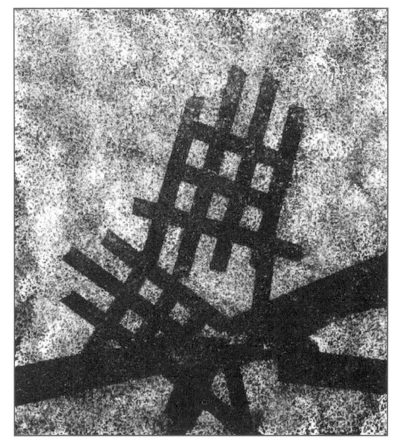

Ground Zero (2023)[3]

Being There

iii.

I stand on the edge, dumbstruck. The stink burns my skin, my eyes, and chokes off my breath. This grand canyon was the World Trade Center—apocalypsed girders and Everests of broken concrete and steel. Brown cumulus smoke blocks sunlight. Burnt wiring and death. Bulldozers scoop and load trucks taking the cement, human pieces, and ash to morgue tents set up in Fresh Kills dump field on Staten Island.[3]

You can always shock, and sometimes you have to do so to capture the truth of the scene as you see it. But shock is both harmful and never enough. It must be deployed compassionately.

Move quickly to find something to contribute beyond the scene itself. If you've chosen to write or express aesthetically an experience, it means something to you. What drives you to share difficult experiences with others? What is the message within the scene? That's what you have to get to.

2. Extract lessons to be learned.

I tried something new, at least for me, in *Ground Zero*. As a set of series of 5-10 poetic or prose pieces of similar form following specific topics, the book allowed liberties, not only of form, but of perspective, voice, and even time. I wanted to address the issues of political mismanagement, particularly how the unintended consequences of expeditious (read that "stupid") brought about far worse injury and death than the original attack. The problem was that I didn't want to turn out a polemic, and I did want to maintain the setting. I wanted to record my experience at the time, yet allow comment on how things played out over the years.

My solution was to give voice to the many people I met at the time—on the streets of Lower Manhattan, in the fire houses, schools, and clinics—who had grave reservations about the emerging response. As a literary device, I set up imaginary confessionals on the street. These persona poetics, "Street Confessionals," were things I'd heard many say at the time, selected for their prescience of misadventures to come.

Confessions 10-12 (2023)[4]

Confessions 10-12

x.

We confess our group amnesia. Will we let our leaders prematurely boast of a "mission accomplished," long before the dying is complete? Help us to stand up when we see our representatives doing wrong.

xi.

We try to remember that strength of character is measured less by impulse and bravado, and more by acceptance of responsibility for the effects of our actions. May we find the strength to acknowledge our limits and weaknesses. Help us to act as if it matters what we do or fail to do.

xii.

We know that how we react to our many 9/11s may prove our own and our nations' end of days. We know that we already have far more than we need. We know that by taking from others is addiction, not virtue. May we somehow find the strength to speak truth and be light, to open our eyes and to see.[4]

Capturing a scene and finding the lessons within it is better than mere sensationalist journalism, but still not enough. If readers are going to get more than illustration of a previously unappreciated corner of the world, as well as a derived critique for future action, they still need to get something to have made the reading worthwhile for themselves personally. Their worlds must be lightened, by having read your piece. Giving hope may not be always possible, and can easily come across as saccharine and Pollyanna, or as if you are preaching. Your truth of the situation includes its difficulty, but try to see and set out the possibility of hope. Your practice of doing that in your writing opens that possibility for your readers.

3. We can find light in the dark.

Ground Zero included a set of prose poems termed "Illuminations." During times of despair and anguish, we may run out of reasons to go on. More accurately, we sometimes find the reasons that had previously sustained us wanting, given the overwhelming darkness we face. What used to be enough to pull us beyond, now may seem unrealistic, shallow, or proved invalid by circumstance. Worse, grand rationales, outworn traditions, and subscriptions to pie-in-the-sky-by-and-by assurances seem to serve the preacher more than the flock.

How to end-run disbelief? The literary program of imagism taught an important truth. If the reader makes the connection alluded to in a piece, it is more authentic and useful. The same is true of assurances of the meaning, significance, or value of persistence in the face of overwhelming adversity. Hope is a dish best served indirectly.

Being Light

I could hear the delicate sounds of violin the moment the subway doors opened. By the time I'd gotten up the steps to the street, I saw the source. His street garb was adequate, he appeared shopworn, but he smiled and his playing stopped people to listen. Dropping a few coins, they would mumble a thanks, and move on. After the piece was finished I asked if he made enough to make his time worthwhile.

"Not much," he admitted, "in dollars and cents. But it's really for me. Everybody's lost in the dark these days," he said. "I want to be the light."[5]

Being Light (2023)[5]

It takes courage to point out the positive. We can be accused of naivety, myopia, romantic idealism. Positivity, particularly when unaccompanied by a belief claim, is not an easy sell in this environment. Persist, however, and trust your readers to learn to illuminate their own darkness by bringing their own light.

Imagining Hope

In 2020, at the outset of the COVID-19 shutdown, I embarked upon what became a three-book series, beginning with *Fireflies Against Darkness* (2021). I juxtaposed despairing newscasts countered by stories of individuals overcoming daunting odds in their lives. In *More Fireflies* (2022), I recount the triumph of Etty Hillesum:

XX. Etty's Story

The world has seen countless times of great darkness. The early 1940s in Holland was one of those times, especially if you were Jewish. Etty Hillesum was 27 when the Nazis entered Amsterdam, and like others, Etty kept a diary. In it, through her suffering, she records her spiritual change of heart. Through her diary, we read of her study of central texts of Jewish mysticism, the poetry of Rilke, Meister Eckhart. "I shall not burden myself with my fears," she writes. This young woman, who served as a volunteer social worker in the Westerbork transit camp, who knew she was likely destined for the death camps to the East, practiced a mindfulness to live fully anyway. We witness how she came to see beyond the pain and brutality, to focus upon the beauty and wonder and mystery of the world beyond circumstance, a world that is always still there.[6]

The message? Not just Etty's amazing courage. Despite dawning knowledge that she would be murdered, she chose to live fully anyway. What I hoped to convey in both the Fireflies series and the Ground Zero project was the simple fact that *circumstances are never the whole story.* It is our response, what we do with the situation, that defines it and us. That simple truth lends hope, and is what we can show our readers during these times of deep uncertainty.

This Most Frightening Here and Now

What can we do to rebuild the future when the future itself is in question? How can we take our skills, our motivation, our passion, and turn them to making the world measurably better? The answer isn't easy, but it is blindingly simple. Stop making it worse.

As culture makers we can do that. Through our work, our writing, our art, we must not add to the cynicism and despair, but rather set the stage for our readers, viewers, listeners, to crack open the doors to hope. Ours is a profession that contributes; it affects humans and what they do. Thus, what we produce has a moral valance, and we have a responsibility:

1. We can avoid cynicism, and choose to believe that what we do matters.

2. In our desire to have our work accepted, we can avoid the temptation of the sensational or trendy. We can avoid adding more trivia or effluvium to the environment in hopes of our own success.

3. We can avoid writing violence or destruction as pornographic titillation. We can point to the meaning and significance we see around us. If we look for the positive, we are more likely to see it; this can be a truth we share with others.

4. We can understand that optimism is less a scientific conclusion (only the most deluded would think that) and more a solid strategy. If we act as if things will work out, we won't preclude it happening through choices and actions based upon despair.

5. We can point to the candles in the darkness.

* * *

The year is 2023: Adventure writer Sebastian Junger sits alone at the Au Rendez-Vous des Belges, just across from the Gare du Nord, as instructed. The somewhat disembodied voice over his hotel phone had claimed to be Kirk Douglas's ghost. It was early in the evening so he'd decided to see what was behind all the mysterious cloak and dagger.

A couple gets up and moves over to his table. "Excuse me," *the man reaches out to shake Sebastian's hand,* "I'm Kirk Douglas." *And he was.* "Thank you for coming, I'd like to introduce you to Ms. Andrée de Jongh."

"I'm glad to meet you, Mr. Junger," *said Andrée, shaking his hand.* "I've been following your adventure journalism."

Shaking her hand, Sebastian looks more closely. "I've heard your name before."

"Ms. De Jongh was twenty-three years old, when the Nazis invaded her country, Belgium," *Kirk Douglas explains.* "This 100-pound girl led soldiers and airmen south 600 miles through enemy-held territory, across the Pyrenees to the British consulate in Bilbao."[7]

"Look," *Sebastian holds up a hand,* "you've come to tell me hero stories about WWII? This is 2023."

"Yes, it is," *Andrée replies.* "You write adventure stories, showing people doing courageous things. It is now time for you to talk about the real heroes, the ones who get up every day facing a world they no longer recognize."

"You refer to the political situation, the fear? The new Nazis? Or the cyber-anonymity?"

"All of it." Kirk smiles. "It reminds me of a conversation I had with John Wayne once, early in my career, about being macho. I told him 'if I play a strong man in a film, I look for the moments where he's weak. And if I play a weak character, I look for the moments where he's strong because that's what drama's all about—chiaroscuro, light and shade.'"

"Mr. Junger," he continues, "the real battle you folks are going to be waging in the next few years is the battle for hope, and I'm glad I don't have to be around. But you are, and if you are going to show people how to hold on to hope, you're going to have to tell real stories, that glow in the dark."

Sebastian looks across the Rue de Dunkerque. When he turns back they are gone. He feels the air growing cooler and can hear the night sounds rise.

Links were retrieved on 19 November 2023, and reconfirmed in February 2024.

1. *Seeking Hope,* 2023, painting by Kendall Johnson in his book *Ground Zero: A 9/11 Memoir in Word and Image* (Sasse Museum of Art, 2023). Pages 4-5. Image source:
    ttps://view.publitas.com/inland-empire-museum-of-art/ground_zero/page/4-5

2. Prose poem and painting (#2 in Fragments series) are adapted from *Fragments: An Archeology of Memory* by Kendall Johnson (Inland Empire Museum of Art, 2017). Pages 8-9. Image source:
    https://view.publitas.com/inland-empire-museum-of-art/fragments-an-archeology-of-memory/page/8-9

3. "Being There" and the painting *Ground Zero,* 2023, by Kendall Johnson in his book *Ground Zero: A 9/11 Memoir in Word and Image* (Sasse Museum of Art, 2023). Pages 14-15. Image source: https://view.publitas.com/inland-empire-museum-of-art/ground_zero/page/14-15

4. *Confessions 10-12* (2023), words and painting by Kendall Johnson in his book *Ground Zero* (see Note 3 above). Pages 50-51. Image source: https://view.publitas.com/inland-empire-museum-of-art/ground_zero/page/50-51

5. *Being Light,* 2023, words and painting by Kendall Johnson in his book *Ground Zero* (see Note 3 above). Pages 60-61. Image source: https://view.publitas.com/inland-empire-museum-of-art/ground_zero/page/60-61

6. "Etty's Story" is from Kendall Johnson's book *More Fireflies* (Arroyo Seco Press, 2022), page 21.

7. For details about the co-founder of the Comet Line escape network in occupied Europe (1941-1944), see "Andrée de Jongh, 90, Legend of Belgian Resistance, Dies" by Douglas Martin in *The New York Times* (18 October 2007): https://www.nytimes.com/2007/10/18/world/europe/18jongh.html

iii.

If you average twelve hours a day grasping the world as just so many force fields and little else, it has to affect how you see horses, rocks, trees, and other human beings. Dali showed us worlds like that, as did Van Gogh, Seurat, and Kandinsky. But how do you live there? How do you find home?

xi.

In July 2016, Malaysian photographer Keeow Wee Loong snuck into the 20-kilometer Fukushima Exclusion Zone and found a ghost town frozen in time since 2011. Cars were abandoned, but the automated traffic lights still worked. Store shelves were still covered with stock, and computers were plugged in on tables in the abandoned school building. A March, 2011 calendar hung on a pub wall next to empty shelves.

boats capsized in fields
thyroid cancer in four thousand children
crows line broken bridge

—Adapted from *A Sublime and Tragic Dance: Robert Oppenheimer & the Manhattan Project* by Kendall Johnson and John Brantingham (2018)

Writing to Heal, Part VI:

Incendiaries

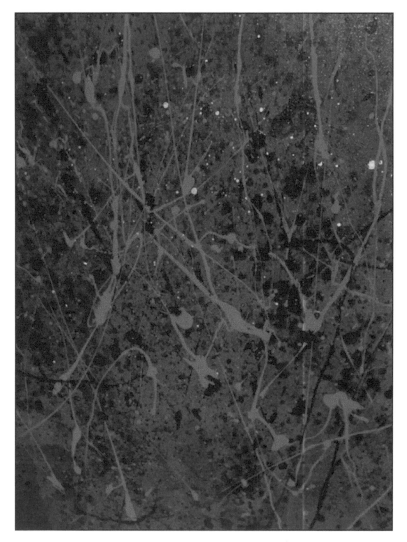

Untitled, 2019 (#1 in Fire series)[1]

Following a twenty-year semi-career as wildland firefighter, then as on-scene trauma consultant to emergency agencies, I have experienced the intensity, terror, and etheric nature of big fires. They both galvanize focused attention, and teach broader perspective. My Fire series attempted to witness primal fire from inside out. This is the glow, the light for which we hunger.

Essay 5 of this Writing to Heal series ends with an imaginary encounter, with the ghost of Kirk Douglas lecturing Sebastien Junger that his adventure stories, if they are to be more than mere empty entertainment during the coming months and years, must be written with purpose, and written in such a way that they "glow in the dark."

We seek fire. The world we write for is now different than it was when we started writing years ago. I recall another time I found things had changed. After a twenty-year hiatus, mid-career in my teaching, I returned to teach at a specialized school for children facing both mentally and physically disabling conditions compounded by significant health challenges. While briefing me on the new composition of my class, the hardened school nurse repeatedly used the term "AFU." Unfamiliar with the word, I asked for clarification. "All Fucked Up," she replied, implying multiple, largely intractably entangled, confounding complications. For all her political incorrectness, there was a grain of truth. Now, as writers, we seem to be facing a world which fits that nurse's estimate. The questions we face, though, are the following: However problematic the world we write to, how do we want to leave it? Can we add constructively to the world, rather than leave it more of a mess?

How do we write meaningfully to a jaded, pandemic-y, post-January 6, perpetual-war-ish, not-so-brave new world that hungers for light but is so ramped up it can't notice much that is subtle? Answer: light a fire. Poke, prod, and tweak people to prompt reflection. Capture the fire of your own authentic experiences—a resource far more powerful than a thousand literary tricks—that can invite attention and reveal truths. The question then becomes, how can we do it safely? Carefully—as our personal, lived adventures, told well, sometimes burn hot enough to illuminate darkness. We must write content that counts, but in a way that is nontoxic. Among our goals should be the peace and quietude that our souls crave in this clamorous, unstable world.

Incendiaries That Heal

At the end of 2023, my 9/11 project—both exhibit and catalog —was complete.[2] My new Incendiaries project was mid-way, and I found myself stuck, unable to write for several days and with my artwork at a stand-still. In desperation, I consulted my inner group of five, via my journal:

> **Art Journal, 12/27/23**
>
> Me: What's the slowdown?
>
> Child replies: I'm anxious about being able to actually produce something useful, a contribution to the world. Everything seems consequential and I doubt my ability.
>
> Wisdom: I'm having trouble with new perspectives. That's why the Incendiaries collection seems boring, and the FF4 (new Fireflies collection) seemed initially exciting. Now not so much. Ruts? Fear?
>
> Wilding: Yes to both above; moreover, I need to break out, tap the deeper source. I think I've been dreaming in those terms. Maybe that's why the Heidegger papers I got distracted with initially seemed promising this morning.

<u>Spirit</u>: It's interesting, but needs to move beyond personal redemption and social critique. Take it further, tapping into a mysticism.

<u>Artist</u>: Go beyond words, deeds; go into the wild dreaming.

Lots of answers, still some mystery, but after some adjustments in my thinking, the consultation paid off. I discontinued the art work, and moved ahead with the writing. I got back on track, but the new track was fresh, new and improved. But what about this magical team? Who are those consultants, you might ask. How much did they cost?

The short answer is: they are all me. And they are expensive, but the price is paid only in the blood, sweat, and years of practice. The long answer, however, the interesting one, takes some digging.

Greenleaves Associates (Claremont, California 1978)

Ten years after my return from combat in Vietnam, and in the midst of divorce from my first wife, I sat in a therapist's office and listened to Dr. Courtney Peterson explain how he understood the mind's inner process, a heady mix of Jungian and Gestalt psychology. "The various characters that together make up you," he pointed out, "sit around a long conference table. Sitting there are your self at key moments growing up, your mother and father, several people who influenced who you've become, and a scattering of archetypal folks who are products of your particular culture. The morning mail is dropped on the table, and your various 'selves' negotiate decisions based upon each issue raised."

[continued on next page]

Later, Peterson elaborated this idea of "inner selves" in more dynamic fashion, and I subsequently used it in my own practice as a therapist and teacher, as well as in some of my writing. The point was to surface the quiet voices inherent within, thus allowing more solid decisions based on a wider, and more adequate perspective.

Lately, I have had the privilege of discussing a wide range of issues with poet and theologian Joy Ladin, who used the concept of voices (re: Bakhtin) in her study of Emily Dickinson[3] and in her award-winning *The Book of Anna*. (See Part 3 of this Writing to Heal series.[4]) In addition, I've spoken with Tony Barnstone, who employs the strategy of giving literary voice to widely discrepant persons he has interviewed or researched, to lend perspective to his work, in particular *Tongue of War*, 2009. (See our conversation in Issues 17 and 18 of *MacQueen's Quinterly*.[5])

These two folks, Joy Ladin and Tony Barnstone, underscore the usefulness of polyphony in weaving together that which is complex.

Our world's gyroscope is beginning to wobble. At times like this we are called to contribute to the stability, to move beyond passive acceptance in our work. We need approaches that can encompass that layered complexity.

Dreaming Oppenheimer (2016)[6]

Oppenheimer, for better or worse, shaped the present age. As the atomic scientists' Doomsday Clock reveals, we teeter 90 seconds from midnight.[7] If we aren't keeping track of the phrase "going nuclear," then we should. What we say in our writing becomes part of the world; Shiva lies in our shadow and haunts our days.

My Personal Inner Group

Over the years I have evolved a fairly concise list of the main players of my Inner Group, certainly those five "voices," or in psycho-jargon, "sub-personalities," most useful to me in exploring ideas, memories, or even future writing. Basically, I summon the group, then ask their response, as I demonstrated at the outset of this essay. Sometimes I employ Registered Art Therapist Lucia Capacchione's technique of writing or drawing with the non-dominant hand to facilitate this inner conversation (*The Power of Your Other Hand*; Red Wheel/ Weiser Press, 2019). To illustrate, I'll let the sub-personalities speak for themselves about their function:

> **Dear Inner Group: Please share your perspective on our writing/art-making process.**
>
> Inner Child: More than the whiner and crier, I am the dreamer, the voice from within, the call to awaken, to sense the need. I'm the truth teller, the reminder of callings. I'm the speaker of the yearnings and fears that lie below the surface impulse and conditioning. I dance between archetype and long term desire.
>
> Inner Wisdom: I'm less about wisdom per se, and more about perspective, strategy, and overview. My job is to size up the resources available. Then, given the goals, to anticipate which path to take through thicket and forest, storm and adversity. Mine is the practical concern, the logistics, the mapmaking. I search the way.
>
> Inner Wilding: I'm not about chaos or sheer impulse. Quite the contrary. I am the breaker of convention, the sound of beyond. I disrupt the ordinary and habitual. I'm the clearest connection to the body's greater logic, the natural flow, the inner river flowing toward the great sea.

<u>Inner Spirit</u>: I am the God of my childhood, the accompanying personal presence some call the great guardian, the amalgam of parents, ancestors, past and future. I am the traditional sun god, the revolutionary feminine Shekinah, the higher self, the conscience, the future toward which we evolve. I am the ocean beyond.

<u>Inner Artist</u>: I am creator, the puller-together of aesthetic perception, the composer of music, the interface with the materials that can give voice to desire. I combine color and value, texture and depth, quiet and loud. I orchestrate movement and production, the paint and the words. I give surface to dreams.

When I run into a situation requiring their input, I simply ask, and then consider the answers. That's what was going on in the 12/27 Art Journal entry at the beginning of this conversation. I can't always predict what will come of it, but it's usually interesting, informative, and often insightful. Through reflection we often find the paths we need to walk.

[continued on next page]

Transfiguration (2016)[8]

The Melting Into Air series explores the nature of the desert experience and its inherent transformational possibilities. From the earliest times, people from different cultures and paths have immersed themselves in the extremes of the place of great undoing (Ryan Kuja[9]) to flee from conventional limitations and to get closer to spiritual truth.

Ground Zero Reflections

In writing *Ground Zero* pieces,[2] I was able to employ my Inner Group dialogue both to explore and write poetic pieces to accompany the art. Having worked with New York crisis teams in the 1990s, and then being called back to provide support to one of the teams (in Lower Manhattan) and an assortment of emergency personnel for several years following the attack on the World Trade Center on 9/11/2001, I had a backlog of imagery and incidents of my own to draw upon for a set of thirty paintings accompanied by text. Many years had passed since the attack, and the material had finally cooled enough for me to work with it in-depth. To do so, I would regularly turn to my Inner Group to help sort through impressions, retrieve memories, and glean through lessons I felt could be learned from such a process. I employed my Inner Group dialogue during the *Ground Zero* projects in two ways: exploration/generation of content, and formulating text/images during writing and artwork.

Examples of Exploring and Generating

The inner dialogue presented at the outset of this discussion shows one use, as I sorted out a muddle that had resulted in a writer's block. Other uses are more related to generating approaches to my work. Again, a journal sample:

> ### 10/29/23, a dream last night
>
> With the world falling away, war deepening in the Middle East, the shift in global threat, the environment still crashing, I dream of a dear friend. In the face of cancer, she has had a breast removed, and is telling me her story. I reply in joyful terms, how she is taking arms against a deadly foe, bold action to keep herself alive. She is disappointed in my response, as are her

friends, who turn away. She had needed me to hear her fear and her pain. I had been deaf to her sorrow.

> Worlds in maelstrom, wolves closing in
> grand narratives miss reality; we must not
> abandon each other; it matters what we do.

Inner Group?

I Child: The broad perspective, the grand narrative, had missed her reality. As had you.

I Wisdom: Her sorrow was less about losing her breast, as it was about losing you.

I Wilding: The world swirls around us, the wolves are closing in. We must not abandon each other.

I Spirit: Be careful with the book, with your readers, and with those close to you. Take good care with what you do.

I Artist: Instead of singular figures in my maelstroms, each painting, each writing, should portray at least two. (See opening image in Essay 5, "Writing Hope," on page 74.)

Formulating Text Using Voices

More than occasionally, I've found the perspectives embodied in my inner-group "voices" helpful in writing actual text for projects. In the midst of the Ground Zero writing, I wasn't sure how best to respond in written form to two of the abstract, but rather intense paintings I'd done. Responses tumbled out quickly, and I realized they built upon one another.

Dear IG: What about the two new paintings?

iChild: We fly above the broken things,

iSpirit: not to avoid or escape, but to reach further

iWisdom: into the heart of things, of each of us

iWilding: a wild leap of ultimate faith reveals

iArtist: our own wild hearts as well.

In verse form:

We fly above the broken things,
not to avoid or escape, but to reach
further into the heart of things,
of each of us a wild leap of faith
reveals our own wild hearts as well.

Or in prose form:

We fly above the broken things, not to avoid or escape, but to reach further into the heart of things, of each of us. A wild leap of ultimate faith reveals our own wild hearts as well.

Or, as revised to fit the expanded, *Ground Zero* text:

If we are standing at the edge of the pit/abyss, when we see our ephemera in destruction and see eternity there also, we ask what it means to us, what can give our lives hope? Where can we find the angels' fire?

[continued on next page]

Angel Fire (2020)[10]

Angel Fire is a spiritual retreat center in the mountains near Taos (NM), built by the grieving father of Lt. David Westfall, who was killed in combat in Vietnam not long after I was there in 1967. Sometimes I go to Angel Fire to think about significance. The retreat is close to the sky, and the breezes—whether hot or cold—are clean and fresh.

A Current Project: Writing "Incendiaries"

My Ground Zero project created space for follow-up work. All that I had addressed in the 9/11 artwork and writing seemed important about that time, some twenty-five years ago. In that work I had searched for reason to hope in the face of collapse. But now things seem even more grim. Blind political divisiveness, spreading gun violence, climate collapse, digitally enforced anonymity, nuclear proliferation, and threat of world war. Cynicism and hopelessness seem rampant. My need to address these aspects of life in the mid-2020s seems more pressing, echoing the concerns I voiced in the inner-voice dialogue of 12/27/23, at the outset of this discussion. As 2024 dawns, I am working on a set of reflections to be included in a collaborative collection with writers John Brantingham, Kate Flannery, and poet/artist Jane Edberg, all of us affiliated with the *Journal of Radical Wonder*. In this collection, we focus our reflections on the events of Fall 2023, juxtaposed against the necessary process of opening to the wild space both outside and within.

I call my own contribution to this collection, "Incendiaries." My writing attempts to capture events from October through December, and reflect on their two-fold nature. They are at once moments of events occurring in the world, and at the same time media spectacles spun to keep us mesmerized by television and political clamor. This Janus-head reality leaves us perpetually anxious and disconnected from our deeper selves. My Incendiaries attempt to locate our concerns and discontent and set the stage for the alternative world available to soothe our spirits and restore our sense of reality. Our world may be falling away, but we must refocus on the bigger picture, if we are to take effective action, avoid despair, and survive.

[continued on next page]

Inner Group Guides My Incendiaries

To illustrate my writing project during this time, I will track some of my writing process using my inner group.

1. The original form of writing was an inner-group collaboration. The first part would be the prompt; the second would be a memoir-based association of similar circumstance I had experienced in the past that provided a parallel, an insight, or perhaps an extreme consequence that foreshadowed a risk in the present circumstance. The third element was a prayer from one of the diverse world religions that addressed values inherent in the present circumstance that could provide perspective. The final element was the sense I could bring to the present situation, based upon prior experience or spiritual dimension. It became clear that the elements interacted much as a sonnet form might, with a volta leading to broadening shift of perspective. I developed a template I could use when analyzing the news item that would lead to articulating the elements consistently.

2. Prompt. Unfortunately, with all in the world that's wobbling out of control, writing prompts arrive daily on the morning news. A sensitive soul, I can't bear a full TV newscast, so I skim headlines on a news aggregate. When I find something that tugs at my heart, I copy and paste the article, and open another blank document. Sometimes links lead to information more important than the original prompt.

3. The template would then guide the thinking and writing about the newscast.

4. The often unwieldy rough draft would be worked to tighten the writing.

After 10-15 of these, it became apparent that they were far too wordy, and begged for revision into more concise form. Again consultation with the Inner Group resulted in dropping the memoir section from each piece, and using that element simply to inform the rest. In several of the twenty or so pieces that are complete, explicit mention of the memoir element is apparent in only a few.

The final versions were further tightened to roughly 100 words, partly to render them more compatible with the other two writers' adjacent prose poems with which my pieces were matched, and partly because each piece seemed stronger, more "incandescent" in its shorter version.

Example: Writing to Gaza

On the morning of October 12, 2023, various news agencies reported an incident of hate-motivated violence in Plainfield, Illinois. Upset by the implications of the event, I consulted the "inner group" for guidance in how to capture the event, my reactions to the incident, and what sense to make of it in terms of a larger picture. The resulting set of considerations from the five perspectives were woven into the following template.

1. A summary of the incident as reported
2. A memoir of a similar incident I experienced years ago
3. A relevant spiritual writing
4. A commentary that pointed beyond the incident itself

Utilizing that template, I began by sorting the story, and my reaction to it, into the following components:

[continued on next page]

Prayers for Morning, #1
October 17, 2023

Plainfield, Illinois

Family and friends gather holding vigil for a Muslim mother hospitalized from a knife attack in her own home, her 6-year-old dead. The reason: her attacker "was upset" at events far distant in the Middle East, in a war unleashed by longstanding hate.

In Yokosuka long ago, some twenty years following the nuclear bombs, I watched drunk sailors and marines on night's liberty screaming and cursing, raging dogs spitting through windows at Japanese citizens walking by, candles lit in silent protest.

…the people living across the ocean surrounding us, I believe, are all our brothers and sisters. A Shinto prayer for peace.

We, who are blessed with the capability for greatness
regularly descend into madness, striking and maiming,
murdering all before us, going berserk in ways that would shame
the most fearsome and ferocious animal in the wild.

While this captured much of the event for me, I found the memoir essential, but the Shinto prayer better left implicit. The piece also lacked the poignancy of the cause for the protest. I then went further and tightened it into the following, and for me more satisfying, prose poem:

Plainfield, Illinois

Family and friends hold vigil for a Muslim mother hospitalized from a knife wound. Her attacker stated he "was upset" at events in the Middle East. In Yokosuka long ago, I watched drunken sailors screaming and cursing at Japanese citizens passing, candles lit in silent prayer against the nuclear carrier just offshore. Our capacity for greatness notwithstanding, we regularly run amok, go berserk in ways that would shame even the most fearsome animals in the wild.

This resulting short piece feels to me stronger than the longer version, partly because it is informed by the elements contained in the template. I believe it has more "glow."

The fire alone is not enough, however, as witnessed by the current incendiary, political rhetoric and spectacular media. My final consideration is the effect of what I've written upon those who read it. However true the writing is to me, I must ask myself whether it should be shared. This opens the issue of ethics, and my, our, responsibility for the effects of the writing and art on others.

[continued on next page]

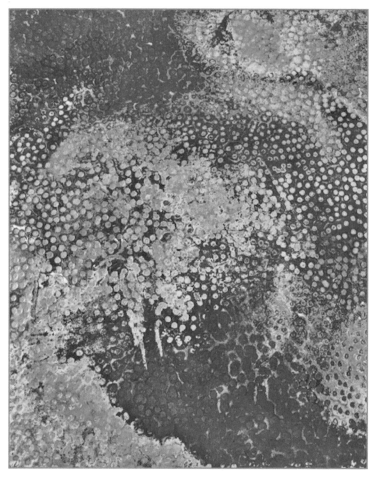

Aboriginal Fires Next Time (2021)[11]

"Dreamtime" refers to the Australian Aboriginal prehistorical time of origin of the world and people. The Dreaming explains how things were and are formed, how we got here, and the ways we should live. The fires of the cosmos are part of this drama, and our writing about such things could, and should, attempt to reflect and to pull us toward an aesthetic of an indigenous vision of respect and responsibility for all things. We must dream our world.

Incendiary Ethics

2024 may prove to be a year of great reckoning. Notions of truth and reason may be held responsible, democracy may become reestablished, accountability may re-emerge a viable option, reality may once again become a standard. If that is to be, though, writers and other artists will need to assist in the rebuild. We are called to do more with our work than simply make money or build our personal résumé.

Worlds can be built and destroyed by words. The hows, whats, and whys we create, have consequences. Literary devices, for example, are used to sell cars, provide distraction, and, as we have seen lately, prompt irrational acts. When you put your writing into the world, be mindful of its effects.

1. **Do No Harm.** Beware of unintended consequences when choosing content and language.

2. **Consider Interpretation.** What we tell others may be taken seriously and may prompt actions that were previously held in check. This may be good or bad, creating or destroying the best for the world.

3. **Empower Readers.** Give their inner sense of perspective cause for hope. We naturally seek some things which may be desirable but unlikely. During uncertain times, it is tempting to try to avoid risk. Yet holding on to hope creates greater likelihood of making the less likely happen.

4. **Balance Needs.** If we are to write about pain or suffering, we need to write with an authentic voice, particularly if we write from our own experience. Our writing rings truer, and that can be therapeutic for the writer. If our writing is to be worthwhile, however, we must do more than simply add to the negativity of

the world. We must find ways for our writing to be redemptive, and make it healing for our readers as well.

5. **Model Courage.** We must hold up real models of courage, facing this moment's uncertainties. These models must be untainted by cultural platitudes and cartoon characterizations.

6. **Nurture Spirit.** Speak of the flowering of the deep within. Listen to, and demonstrate, your own inner spirit.

7. **Speak Truth.** Show overcoming challenge by being true to your felt experience and deepest and strongest self.

It matters what we do. We bring vast resources to our writing, including the things we know and the strategies we've learned. They strengthen our writing. Our writing can help as well as hurt. Used wisely and ethically, our command of incendiary writing can make our contributions to the world glow in the darkness and generate light.

Links were retrieved on 27 January 2024, with the exception of the link for Note 3 ("Supposed Persons...") which was retrieved on 5 February 2024. All links were reconfirmed in February 2024.

1. Untitled, 2019 (#1 in Fire series), painting by Kendall Johnson.

2. *Ground Zero: A 9/11 Memoir in Word and Image* by Kendall Johnson (Sasse Museum of Art, 2023):
   https://view.publitas.com/inland-empire-museum-of-art/ground_zero/page/1

3. "Supposed Persons: Emily Dickinson and 'I'" by Joy Ladin in *The Emily Dickinson International Society Bulletin*, 25:1 (May/June 2013): https://www.academia.edu/5870293/ Supposed_Persons_Emily_Dickinson_and_I

4. See the final three sections of "Writing to Heal, Part 3: Forms for Healing" in this book: "Joy Ladin and Voicing Parts" (page 46), "Progressing Through the Belly of the Beast" (page 48), and "Forming Good Writing" (page 51).

5. "A Conversation with Tony Barnstone: Writing Difficult Material" by Kendall Johnson, with Part I in Issue 17 of *MacQueen's Quinterly*: http://www.macqueensquinterly.com/MacQ17/Johnson-Interview-Barnstone.aspx

   And Part II in Issue 18: http://www.macqueensquinterly.com/MacQ18/Johnson-Interview-Barnstone-Part-2

6. *Dreaming Oppenheimer*, 2016 by Kendall Johnson in *A Sublime and Tragic Dance* by Kendall Johnson & John Brantingham (Cholla Needles Press, 2016).

7. "A moment of historic danger: It is still 90 seconds to midnight," the 2024 Doomsday Clock Statement from the Science and Security Board, in *Bulletin of the Atomic Scientists* (23 January 2024): https://thebulletin.org/doomsday-clock/current-time/

8. *Transfiguration*, 2016 (Melting Into Air series), painting by Kendall Johnson.

9. "Desert Spirituality: 'The Place of Great Undoing'" by Ryan Kuja, excerpted from his book *From the Inside Out: Reimagining Mission, Recreating the World* at SDI Companions.org (26 June 2019): https://www.sdicompanions.org/desert-spirituality-the-place-of-great-undoing/

[continued on next page]

10. *Angel Fire*, 2020 (Melting Into Air series), acrylic on photo transfer by Kendall Johnson. Appears here courtesy of Roberta and Michael Baumann.

11. *Aboriginal Fires Next Time*, 2021; photograph shot through vintage window in Winslow, AZ by Kendall Johnson.

The six essays in this Writing to Heal series are reprinted here from the online arts and literary journal *MacQueen's Quinterly*:

Part I:
"Tapping Hidden Gifts of Experience" in Issue 16 (1 January 2023)

Part II:
"Diving Deep" in Issue 17 (29 January 2023)

Part III:
"Forms for Healing" in Issue 18 (29 April 2023)

Part IV:
"Through a Curatorial Eye: The Apocalypse This Time" in Issue 19 (15 August 2023)

Part V:
"Writing Hope" in the Gratitude Issue, 20X (21 November 2023)

Part VI:
"Incendiaries" in Issue 22 (4 February 2024)

End Notes

Writing can heal. It shares that magic with painting, movement, and music, and it pulls from us layers that we can access, sometimes in no other way…. Write your truth. Write to heal; heal to write.

—Kendall Johnson

x.

I know it is time to spread my wings upward, to join with the sunrise, the world's risings and meltings. Time to pass on the significance I have found, to add my best light to these ten thousand stars.

It matters that publisher Clare MacQueen transforms others' best written and artistic works into collective visions for others.

Acknowledgments

Many thanks to the following:

Sasse Museum of Art for images

Clare MacQueen for her continued encouragement

Kate Flannery and John Brantingham for their
valued writing support

Thomas R. Thomas, Arroyo Seco Press,
for the Fireflies series

Artworks, in Order of Appearance

Twenty of Kendall Johnson's artworks appear in this book. And ceramic art by Morty Bachar is featured on the title page, a Kintsugi bowl whose symbolism Dr. Johnson finds especially meaningful.

With three exceptions (see footnotes on next page), images herein are provided courtesy of Sasse Museum of Art in Pomona, California.

Untitled, 2022 (M-15, Melting Into Air series)

Image appears across the front and back covers.

Page	Description

---

1. Photograph provided by Morty Bachar and Lakeside Pottery.
2. Photograph provided by Kendall Johnson.
3. Image appears herein courtesy of Roberta and Michael Baumann.

I've been broken by the world, I'll admit. Stronger now at some of my broken places, yet scarred in many ways…. As teacher, trauma therapist, and on-scene crisis consultant, my icon—my guiding hope—has been the kintsugi image: a broken ceramic bowl with the parts glued back together, the scars and seams shining with resin and gold. Writing and art have been my salvation.

—Kendall Johnson

Broken bowl restored via Kintsugi process by Morty Bachar,
Lakeside Pottery Studio | https://lakesidepottery.com/

Fascinating video of the restoration above is available on Lakeside Pottery's
YouTube channel: https://www.youtube.com/watch?v=RzSAkFcC10g

Ceramic Artist's Bio

Morty Bachar has an extensive background in engineering and product design. Also an accomplished ceramic artist, ceramic instructor, and art restorer, he performs ceramic and sculpture repair and restoration for individuals, collectors, dealers, and museums. In addition, he designs and creates custom pottery work on commission and to further his passion for Kintsugi art.

The U.S. Department of State commissioned Bachar to create Kintsugi art for President Joe Biden to present to Japanese Prime Minister Yoshihide Suga during his April 2021 visit to the White House. As Bachar said in this excerpt from "Lewes artist creates presidential gift for Japanese prime minister" (*Cape Gazette*, 21 April 2021):

> *I am delighted to see the Kintsugi metaphor now part of international affairs as a symbol of renewal and healing…. Kintsugi gives new life or rebirth to damaged or aging ceramic objects by celebrating their flaws and history. One can consider how we might live a kintsugi life, finding value in the missing pieces, cracks, and chips; bringing to light the scars that have come from life experiences; finding new purpose and meaning through aging and loss; seeing love and the beauty of imperfection; and loving ourselves, family, friends, and country, even with flaws.*

Morty Bachar and his wife, Patty Storms, also a ceramic artist, painter, and sculptor, own and manage Lakeside Pottery, established in 2001 and located in Lewes, Delaware (USA). Morty and Patty combine their many years of experience in teaching art, pottery, sculpting, engineering, and painting, to operate their studios:

https://www.lakesidepottery.com/

Author's Bio

Photograph © copyrighted 2024 by Susan Ilsley

Dr. Kendall Johnson grew up in the lemon groves in Southern California, raised by assorted coyotes and bobcats. A former firefighter with military experience, he served as a therapist and crisis consultant—often in the field. As a psychologist and trauma specialist, he has written several non-fiction books and numerous articles on trauma and school crisis. He trained crisis teams and rendered direct support following numerous school shootings, natural disasters, and 9/11.

As a nationally certified teacher, he taught art and writing, served as a gallery director, and still serves on the board of the Sasse Museum of Art, for whom he authored the museum books *Fragments: An*

Archeology of Memory (2017), an attempt to use art and writing to retrieve lost memories of combat, and *Dear Vincent: A Psychologist Turned Artist Writes Back to Van Gogh* (2020). He holds national board certification as an art teacher for adolescents to young adults.

Dr. Johnson retired from teaching and clinical work in 2022 to pursue painting, photography, and writing full time. In that capacity he has written five literary books of artwork and poetry, and one in art history. His memoir collection, *Chaos & Ash*, was released from Pelekinesis in 2020, his *Black Box Poetics* from Bamboo Dart Press in 2021, and his *The Stardust Mirage* from Cholla Needles Press in 2022. His Fireflies series is published by Arroyo Seco Press: *Fireflies Against Darkness* (2021), *More Fireflies* (2022), and *The Fireflies Around Us* (2023).

Kendall's shorter work has appeared in *Chiron Review, Cultural Weekly, Literary Hub, MacQueen's Quinterly, Quarks Ediciones Digitales,* and *Shark Reef,* and was translated into Chinese by *Poetry Hall: A Chinese and English Bi-Lingual Journal.* He serves as contributing editor for the *Journal of Radical Wonder.*

Author's email address: layeredmeaning@gmail.com

Author's website: http://www.layeredmeaning.com

And several of Kendall's "Fireflies" in *The Journal of Radical Wonder*: https://medium.com/the-journal-of-radical-wonder/tagged/kendall-johnson

Editor's Bio

Clare MacQueen is founding editor, curator, and publisher of *MacQueen's Quinterly,* aka MacQ, launched online on New Year's Day 2020, and its precursor literary and arts journal, *KYSO Flash* (2014-2019). She edited, designed, and produced 20 printed books, including six annual anthologies, via KYSO Flash Press (retired March 2020). In Autumn 2023, she collaborated with Alexis Rhone Fancher and Kenna Barradell to produce *Triggered: A Pillow Book,* via MacQ.

Clare is co-editor, with Lorette C. Luzajic, of *The Memory Palace: An Ekphrastic Anthology* (2024). As the webmaster and an associate editor for *Serving House Journal* (2010-2018), she assisted with publishing 18 online issues. And she's one of four co-editors of *Steve Kowit: This Unspeakably Marvelous Life* (Serving House Books, 2015).

She was also honored to serve as one of three finalist judges for the Jack Grapes Poetry Prize in 2021, and as one of two judges for the 2017 Steve Kowit Poetry Prize. For several years, she's been a member of the Senior General Advisory Board for *Best Small Fictions.*

After living and working 16 years in San Diego and 25 years in the northern Puget Sound area, Clare left the West Coast three years ago due to family illness, and returned to North Carolina where her family had settled during her teens 50 years ago. Though she now lives near Winston-Salem, her heart remains in the Pacific Northwest.

www.macqueensquinterly.com